PRACTICAL EL

Other Titles of Interest

PRACTICAL ELECTRONIC DESIGN DATA

by

Owen Bishop

BERNARD BABANI (publishing) LTD
THE GRAMPIANS
SHEPHERDS BUSH

Please Note

Although every care has been taken with the production of this book to ensure that any projects, designs, modifications and/or programs etc. contained herewith, operate in a correct and safe manner and also that any components specified are normally available in Great Britain, the Publishers and Author do not accept responsibility in any way for the failure, including fault in design, of any project, design, modification or program to work correctly or to cause damage to any other equipment that it may be connected to or used in conjunction with, or in respect of any other damage or injury that may be so caused, nor do the Publishers accept responsibility in any way for the failure to obtain specified components.

Notice is also given that if equipment that is still under warranty is modified in any way or used or connected with home-built equipment then that warranty may be void.

First Published — June 1992

British Library Cataloguing in Publication Data
Bishop, O. N.
    Practical Electronic Design Data
    I. Title
    621.381

    ISBN 0 85934 316 2

Contents

Chapter 1

UNITS

1 Definitions
The subheadings in this section give:

the *name* of the unit
the *symbol* for the unit
the *physical quantity* that the unit measures
the *symbol* used for the physical quantity in equations.

Symbols for units are always printed in roman (upright) letters, but symbols for quantities are printed in italic (sloping) letters.

Ampere (= amp) A current I
Fundamental electrical unit, measured by the force (in newtons) between two conductors or coils of given dimensions (in metres) placed a given distance apart (in metres).

Coulomb C charge Q
One coulomb of charge passes a point in a circuit when a current of 1 ampere flows for 1 second.

$$\text{charge} = \text{current} \times \text{time} \quad Q = It \text{ or } I = \frac{Q}{t}$$

Volt V potential V
The potential at any point in space is defined as the work done (in joules) in bringing a unit charge (1C) to that point from an infinite distance.

Usually, when we refer to the potential at a point we really mean the potential *difference* relative to some other point which we consider to be at zero potential (0V). Often the reference potential is earth or 'ground' potential. Sometimes it is the potential of the so-called 'negative' terminal of a battery. The potential of a point is considered to be positive if work has to be done to move a positive charge toward it. In most instances the 'points' referred to above are locations within an electrical circuit.

$$\text{potential} = \frac{\text{energy}}{\text{charge}} \quad V = \frac{J}{Q}$$

The *electromotive force* (e.m.f.) of a source of potential such as an electric cell or generator is the p.d. between its terminals measured when no current is flowing. If the cell or generator is connected to an electric circuit so that current flows through the circuit, there is a drop of potential across the internal resistance of the cell or generator itself. Therefore the p.d. between its terminals is less than its e.m.f. The larger the current, the less the p.d. (Fig.1). E.m.f. is sometimes represented by the symbol E.

Ohm Ω impedance Z
reactance X
resistance R

For definitions of impedance and reactance, see pages 144 and 146. When a current I flows through a conductor, the resistance of the conductor causes electrical energy to be converted to thermal energy. This results in a fall in potential along the conductor, resulting a p.d. V between its ends. The resistance R of the conductor is defined by:

$$\text{resistance} = \frac{\text{p.d.}}{\text{current}} \quad R = \frac{V}{I}$$

Other forms of the above equation are:

$$V = IR \quad \text{and} \quad I = \frac{V}{R}$$

Watt W power P

Power is the rate at which work is done when energy is converted from one form into another. In conversions which

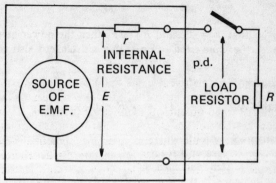

CELL or GENERATOR

SOURCE OF E.M.F.

r INTERNAL RESISTANCE

E

p.d.

LOAD RESISTOR R

(a)

$$I = 0 \qquad V_r = Ir = 0$$

$$\text{p.d.} = E - V_r = E$$

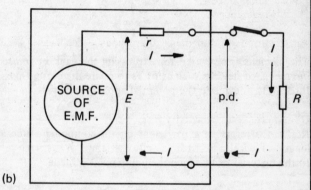

SOURCE OF E.M.F.

r

$I \rightarrow$

E

I

p.d.

R

$\leftarrow I$

$\leftarrow I$

(b)

$$V_r = I \times r$$

$$\text{p.d.} = E - V_r = E - I \times r$$

Fig.1   *The relationship between the e.m.f. and terminal p.d. of a cell or generator. Part of the e.m.f. is dropped across the internal resistance when current flows: (a) no current; (b) current is flowing*

involve electric current:

$$P = IV$$

Given that $V = IR$ and $P = IV$, then the power being dissipated (i.e. converted to heat) in a resistance is also given by:

$$P = IV = I \times IR = I^2R$$

Similarly, $\qquad P = IV = V/R \times V = V^2/R$

Siemens S   **admittance** Y
                  susceptance B
                  conductance G

Conductance is the inverse of resistance. An older name for the unit is the *mho*. For definitions of admittance and susceptance see pages 146 and 147.

$$G = \frac{I}{V}$$

The siemens is also used for expressing the gain, or *transconductance*, of devices such as FETs to relate the current passing through the device to the potential applied to its gate.

Ohm-metre Ω**m**   **resistivity** ρ

Resistance refers to a particular circuit component such as a length of wire, a resistor, a cell or a lamp. *Resistivity* refers to the material from which the component is made.

$$\text{resistance}, R = \frac{\rho \ell}{A}$$

where A is the cross-sectional area of the conductor, in square metres, and ℓ is its length, in metres.

Farad F   **capacitance** C

As charge flows into a capacitor or other device having capacitance, a p.d. builds up across that device. The capacitance C is defined by:

$$\text{capacitance} = \frac{\text{charge}}{\text{p.d.}} \qquad C = \frac{Q}{V}$$

Tesla T   magnetic flux density B

Also known as the *magnetic field*. If a conductor length ℓ is carrying a current I and the angle between the field of magnetic flux B and the conductor is θ, the force F (in newtons) on the wire is given by:

$$F = BI . \ell \sin \theta$$

The force in the direction at right angles to the field (when $\theta = 90°$) is $F = BI . \ell$.

For a circular coil of N turns, radius r the magnetic flux density at the centre of the coil is:

$$B = \mu_0 NI/2r$$

where μ_0 is the permeability of free space and has the value of $4\pi \times 10^{-7} = 1.2566 \times 10^{-6}$. *Example:* the magnetic flux density at the centre of a circular coil of 25 turns radius 0.05m when a current of 1.5A is flowing is $(1.2566 \times 10^{-6} \times 1.5 \times 25)/(2 \times 0.05) = 4.7 \times 10^{-4}$ T.

At a point on the axis of the coil, distant x from the centre of the coil:

$$B = \frac{\mu_0 NI}{2} \times \frac{r^2}{(r^2 + x^2)^{3/2}}$$

Weber Wb   magnetic flux Φ

If the magnetic flux density is 1T, the magnetic flux is 1Wb per square metre. A magnetic flux of 1Wb linked to a coil of 1 turn produces an e.m.f. of 1V if the flux is reduced to zero in 1s.

Henry H   self-inductance L
mutual inductance M

The self-inductance L of a coil is 1H if a current of 1A passing through the coil produces a magnetic flux of 1Wb:

$$L = N\Phi/I$$

Alternatively, the self inductance is defined as being numerically equal to the e.m.f. induced in the coil when the current changes at the rate of 1A per second:

$$E = -L.\mathrm{d}I/\mathrm{d}t$$

The negative sign indicates that the induced e.m.f. *opposes* any change in the current.

The mutual inductance M of two coils is 1H if a current of 1A in one coil produces a magnetic flux of 1Wb in the other.

$$M = N_\mathrm{s}\Phi_\mathrm{s}/I_\mathrm{p}$$

where suffixes 'p' and 's' refer to the primary and secondary coils.

Alternatively, the mutual inductance is equal to the e.m.f. induced in one coil when the current in the other coil changes at 1A per second.

$$E_\mathrm{s} = -M.\mathrm{d}I_\mathrm{p}/\mathrm{d}t$$

Hertz Hz frequency f
The hertz is defined as 1 event per second. In electronics, frequency is often the number of electrical pulses or the repetitions of a waveform per second.

Kelvin K temperature t
The kelvin is a measure of temperature on the absolute scale, on which 0K is absolute zero ($-273°\mathrm{C}$) and on which 273K equals $0°\mathrm{C}$. To convert from kelvin to degrees Celsius, add 273. As units of temperature *difference* the kelvin and the degree Celsius are identical.

Decibel dB ratio between two quantities n
Given two quantities x_1 and x_2 (which might be two currents or two p.d.s, for example), the ratio between them in decibels is:

$$n = 10 \times \log_{10}(x_2/x_1)$$

2 Multiples of units
Prefix the unit name as follows:

Base unit multiplied by:	Prefix	Symbol	Example
10^3 (thousand)	kilo-	k-	kV, kilovolt
10^6 (million)	Mega-	M-	$M\Omega$, megohm
10^9 (thousand million)	Giga-	G-	GV, gigavolt
10^{12} (million million)	Tera-	T-	$T\Omega$, teraohm

3 Sub-multiples of units
Prefix the unit name as follows:

Base unit divided by:	Prefix	Symbol	Example
10^3 (thousandth)	milli-	m-	mS, millisiemens
10^6 (millionth)	micro-	μ-	μH, microhenry
10^9 (thousand millionth)	nano-	n-	nA, nanoamp
10^{12} (million millionth)	pico-	p-	pF, picofarad

4 The main equations relating different units

Resistance

$V = IR$	$I = V/R$	$R = V/I$

Power

$P = IV$	$P = I^2R$	$P = V^2/R$

Charge and capacitance

$Q = It$	$C = Q/V$

Magnetic flux

$$F = BI \,.\, \ell \sin\theta$$

$$B = \mu_0 NI/2r$$

$$B = \frac{\mu_0 NI}{2} \times \frac{r^2}{(r^2 + x^2)^{3/2}}$$

Self inductance

$L = N\Phi/I$ $\qquad\qquad\qquad E = -L.\mathrm{d}I/\mathrm{d}t$

Mutual inductance

$M = N_s\Phi_s/I_p$ $\qquad\qquad\qquad E_s = -M.\mathrm{d}I_p/\mathrm{d}t$

Chapter 2

COMPONENTS

1 Resistors

Resistance value code
On schematic diagrams, in component lists, and often in the text itself resistance values are usually indicated as follows:

ohms – using the ohm symbol (Ω), the letter R,
or no symbol.
Examples: $12\Omega = 12R = 12$: $270\Omega = 270R = 270$.
Ω or R also acts as a decimal point, if required.
Examples: $6\Omega8 = 6R8 = 6.8$.

kilohms – using k.
Examples: 1k2, 56k, 390k.

megohms – using M.
Examples: 1M0, 4M7, 12M.

The value of a resistor is usually indicated by the colour code (see below). In some cases (e.g. on surface-mount resistors) the value is indicated by 3 digits. The first 2 digits represent the first 2 digits of the value. The third digit indicates a multiplier, in powers of 10. For example, the code '273' indicates $27 \times 10^3 = 27k\Omega$.

Resistor values
Fixed resistors are manufactured in a series of values, the commonest of which is the E12 series. This has 12 standard values in each decade:

10   12   15   18   22   27   33   39   47   56   68   82

The series repeats in higher decades (100, 120, etc.) and in lower decades (1.0, 1.2, etc.). Resistors of closer tolerance usually belong to the E24 series, with 24 values per decade.

The E24 series comprises the E12 series, alternating with intermediate values of its own:

10	11	12	13	15	16	18	20	22	24	27	30
33	36	39	43	47	51	56	62	68	75	82	91

Resistors of the closest tolerance are available in two further series, E48 and E96.

Resistor colour code
See Figure 2 for how to read the resistance-value bands. In the 'format' column below, '1' and '2' (and '3') represent the values indicated by the first 2 (or 3) colour bands. The

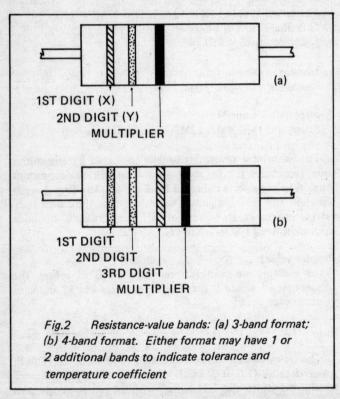

Fig.2   Resistance-value bands: (a) 3-band format; (b) 4-band format. Either format may have 1 or 2 additional bands to indicate tolerance and temperature coefficient

format shows where to place the 'R', 'k' or 'M' in the value, according to the colour of the last band.

Colour	Digit bands	Multiplier band	Format 3-band	Format 4-band
Silver		0.01	0R12	1R23
Gold		0.1	1R2	12R3
Black	0	1	12	123
Brown	1	10	120	1k23
Red	2	100	1k2	12k3
Orange	3	1 000	12k	123k
Yellow	4	10 000	120k	1M23
Green	5	100 000	1M2	12M3
Blue	6	1 000 000	12M	
Violet	7			
Grey	8			
White	9			

Read the 3 (or 4) digits indicated by the digit bands (Fig.2), then multiply by the figure shown in the multiplier band.

Examples:
Red – violet – brown = 27 × 10 = 270Ω   Format 270R
Green – blue – yellow = 56 × 10 000 = 560kΩ Format 560k
Grey – red – red = 82 × 100 = 8200Ω   Format 8k2
Grey – red – black – brown = 820 × 10 = 8200Ω Format 8k2
Blue – grey – gold = 68 × 0.1 = 6.8Ω   Format 6R8

Resistor tolerance code
Indicated by the 4th (or 5th) band, see Figure 2. If the resistor is marked with a 3-digit value code (see above), this may be followed by a letter indicating tolerance:

Colour	Tolerance (%)	Letter
Brown	1	F
Red	2	G
Green	0.5	
Blue	0.25	
Violet	0.1	
Gold	5	J

Colour	Tolerance (%)	Letter
Silver	10	K
No band	20	M

Temperature coefficient code

The temperature coefficient (tempco) is given in parts per million change of resistance per kelvin or degree Celsius. Indicated by the 5th (or 6th) band.

Colour	Tempco
Black	200
Brown	100
Red	50
Orange	25
Yellow	15
Blue	10
Violet	5
Grey	1

Surface mount resistor code

The resistance is indicated by a 3-digit code. The first digits represent the first 2 digits of the value, in ohms. The 3rd digit indicates the number of zeroes following the 2 digits. For example '822' indicates 8200Ω; '430' indicates 43Ω.

Features of different types of fixed resistor

Most types of resistor available today have high stability, high insulation resistance ($1G\Omega$ or more) and low noise ($\leq 0.5\mu V/V$).

Most are intended to operate in the temperature range $-55°C$ to $125°C$.

The codes used in the table below have the following meanings:

Range available

H = high range, $10M\Omega$ or more
N = normal range, lowest is between 1Ω and 10Ω, highest is between $1M\Omega$ and $10M\Omega$.
L = low range, lowest values less than 1Ω.
R = restricted range, only certain values made, usually not the highest or lowest.

Tolerance (given as a percentage)

Power rating
H = 2.5W or more
L = less than 2.5W, down to 0.125W

Working voltage
H = 250V or more, possibly much more
L = less than 250V

Tempco
H = 100 ppm/$^\circ$C or more
L = less than 100 ppm/$^\circ$C

Price
H = more than 5p per resistor
L = 5p or less per resistor

Surface mount resistors are available in two popular sizes: type 1206 measures 3.2mm × 1.6mm, rating at 0.1W; type 0805 measures 2.00mm × 1.25mm. Power resistors are also available.

The listings above are based on typical specifications. Types made by different manufacturers may vary in one or more particulars from the descriptions.

Selecting a resistor

Figure 3 is a flowchart for selecting resistors on the basis of value required, tolerance, power rating, working voltage, and tempco. In selecting a resistor, first note the resistance required and the maximum voltage that is likely to be placed across it. Usually it is sufficient to take the supply voltage as the maximum likely voltage. Calculate the power rating needed, using the formula $P = V^2/R$. If the current is known instead of the voltage, use the formula $P = I^2R$. It is preferable to use a resistor well within its rated power as overheating leads to a change in its resistance. If the resistor is to operate at high temperature, double the calculated power rating for every 30° above 70°C. It is also advisable to double or even quadruple the power-rating and the working voltage rating if

Table 1 – FEATURES OF FIXED RESISTORS

Type	Range	Tolerance	Power rating	Working voltage	Tempco	Price
Carbon film	N	5	L	H	H (negative)	L
Metal film	N	1 or 5	L	H	L	L
Metal film, high volts	N	5	L	H	H	H
Metal film, precision	R	0.1	L	L	L	H
Cermet film	H	5	L	H	H	H
Wire-wound cement case (ceramic body)	R	5 or 10	H	H	H	H
Wire-wound silicon coated	L	5 or 10	H	L	L	H
Wire-wound vitreous enamel	L	5	H	L	L	H
Wire-wound aluminium case	L	5	H*	H	L	H
Wire-wound precision	R	0.1	L	H	L**	H

* may be approximately doubled by use of a heat sink

** thermal e.m.f. is usually less than $0.2\mu V/^{\circ}C$

14

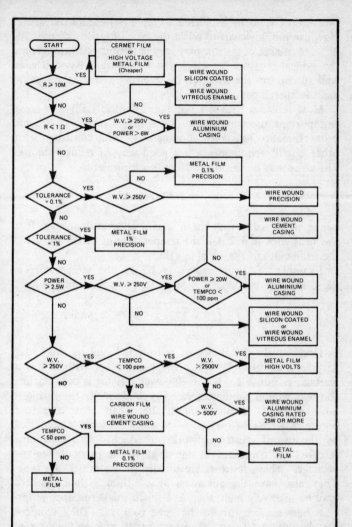

Fig.3 Flowchart for selecting resistors. W.V. = working voltage (max.); TEMPCO = resistance temperature coefficient per °C

the resistor is to be subjected to rapid pulses and transients. Now use the flowchart to select the type of resistor to use. As different makes of resistor may vary in their specification from the typical resistors on which the flowchart is based it is as well to confirm the selection by referring to the catalogue or manufacturer's data sheet.

Most resistors have low noise but, if specifically low noise is important, use wire-wound or metal film resistors. Noise is proportional to resistance, so using a low value consistent with other circuit requirements is a good way of reducing noise. The noise may be calculated from this formula:

$$\text{noise} = 7.43 \sqrt{Rt.\Delta f}$$

where noise is the root mean square value in nanovolts, R is the resistance in kΩ, t is the temperature in kelvin and Δf is the bandwidth of the signal in kHz.

Example: if the resistance is 2.2kΩ, the temperature is 25°C and the bandwidth is 500kHz, the r.m.s. noise voltage is:

$$7.43 \sqrt{2.2 \times (25 + 273) \times 500} = 4254\,\text{nV}$$

Occasionally the choice of resistor is based on small size, to give a compact layout. Select a resistor with as low a wattage as possible. If a high-power resistor is unavoidable, the wire-wound aluminium cased type is usually the smallest. Surface-mount resistors are smaller than their axial-lead equivalents. Space may be saved and PCB layouts simplified by the use of resistor networks, in which 4 to 13 identical resistors are contained in one single-in-line or double-in-line package. These resistors are usually of the metal film type. They also have the advantage that although their tempcos may be relatively high, there is a much smaller tempco difference between resistors in the same package. Their tempcos may be within 50 ppm/°C of each other, making them useful in certain applications, such as potential dividers.

Resistors in series
When two or more resistors are connected in series their total

resistance is the sum of their individual resistances:

$$R_T = R_1 + R_2 + R_3 + \ldots + R_n$$

When resistors of the same tolerance are joined in series, the total resistance has the same tolerance as the individual resistors. The total working voltage is the sum of the individual working voltages. The power rating and tempco remain unchanged.

By joining two E12 resistors in series it is possible to produce equivalents of the E24 series, as shown in this table:

Resistor A	Resistor B											
	10	12	15	18	22	27	33	39	47	56	68	82
10	**20**	22	25	28	32	37	**43**	49	57	66	78	*92*
12		**24**	27	**30**	34	39	45	**51**	59	68	80	94
15			30	33	37	42	48	54	**62**	71	83	97
18				**36**	40	45	**51**	57	65	*74*	86	
22					44	49	55	61	69	78	*90*	
27						54	60	66	*74*	83	95	
33							66	72	80	89		
39								78	86	95		
47									94			

Totals in **bold** type are members of the E24 series; those in *italic* type are close to E24 values. The remaining E24 values in this decade are obtained like this: 11 = 10+1; 13 = 12+1; 16 = 15+1. The same combinations apply in the other decades.

Resistors in parallel

When two or more resistors are joined in parallel, their combined resistance is given by:

$$\frac{1}{R_T} = \frac{1}{R_1} + \frac{1}{R_2} + \frac{1}{R_3} + \ldots + \frac{1}{R_n}$$

For two resistors in parallel, this formula can be simplified to:

$$R_T = \frac{R_1 \times R_2}{R_1 + R_2}$$

If two equal resistors of the same type are connected in parallel, the total resistance is halved and, more importantly, the power rating is doubled. This is a useful way of dealing with high power requirements if a high-wattage resistor is not available. The tolerance remains unaltered.

Variable resistors

Since the tolerance of variable resistors is usually only 20%, most manufacturers produce only 3 values per decade: 10, 22 and 47. The temperature coefficient of most types is usually at least 100 ppm/°C, which is not as low as with certain types of fixed resistor but is adequate for most purposes.

One feature of importance is the resolution, the minimum practicable change in resistance when the spindle is turned. As a rough guide, a turn of 1° can be taken as the minimum angle so, if the electrical rotation of the resistor is 270°, the resolution is 1/270 times the total resistance. See later for resolution of multiturn resistors.

Such a wide range of variable resistors is made that, after considering the points outlined below, the catalogue details should be consulted before deciding which particular type to employ:

Presets (= trimpots): small, intended for mounting on the PCB, adjusted by screwdriver or by small integral knob. The enclosed types are best in a dusty or damp environment. Carbon tracks are cheapest but have a relatively low power rating (usually about 0.15W). Irregularities in the track may mean that resolution is much lower than that calculated by the method described above. Cermet tracks wear much better (so are much less likely to develop contact noise with age), have better resolution, have lower tempco, and generally have a higher power rating (up to 0.5W). Cermets are small and have low self-capacitance, making them useful in high-frequency circuits. When they are being used as a series resistor, trimpots (and pots, see below) should always be used with the wiper connected to one end of the track

(Fig.26). This prevents an open circuit occurring should the wiper lose contact with the track owing to dirt, wear, etc.

Potentiometers (= pots): larger (16 − 30mm diameter), intended for panel mounting and usually have a plain spindle which requires a knob. Available with carbon or cermet tracks (see remarks above). Some cermet potentiometers have 10% tolerance. Cermet pots are available in higher power ratings, up to 5W. Carbon and cermet pots normally have linear tracks, in which equal turns of the spindle produce equal changes in resistance. However a typical pot is likely to depart from linearity by as much as 10%. They are also available with logarithmic tracks in which, as the spindle is turned clockwise, the resistance increases slowly at first and more rapidly later on. These are specially suited to applications such as volume controls in audio equipment, where equal turns of the spindle will produce apparently equal changes in loudness. Because of the subjective nature of loudness, such pots are only nominally logarithmic and typically departures of more than 10% are found. Pots with conductive plastic tracks have low torque (2×10^{-3} Nm) and good linearity. They are suitable for use in servo-mechanisms, except when a rotation of more than about 340° is required. Wire-wound pots were once used for high-power applications but have been largely replaced by cermet types, which have better resolution. They are unsuitable for use in a corrosive environment and, with signals of frequency greater than about 10 kHz, there are problems with the self-inductance of the winding. Their main advantages are low noise, low tempco and close tolerance.

Multiturn pots: these are available with cermet tracks or as wire-wound pots. The latter combine fine resolution with low tempco, but are expensive. The resolution of multiturn pots is much higher than that of the single-turn types described above, since the spindle may rotate as many as 25 times in moving the brush from one end of the track to the other. If V is the voltage between the two ends of the track, and the maximum number of turns is N, the voltage at the wiper changes by $V/360N$ for each degree turn of the spindle.

Slide pots: these are a variant of the carbon track pot, available in linear or logarithmic form. Their special application is that when suitably mounted on a panel the position of the knob gives a visual indication of the setting of the resistor. The use of a bank of such slide pots to control a graphic equalizer is an example of this.

2 Capacitors

Capacitor value code

On schematic diagrams, in component lists and often in the text itself capacitance values are usually indicated by using the symbols p, n, and μ to act as a decimal point. *Examples:* 10p represents 10pF, 2n2 represents 2.2nF and 4μ7 represents 4.7μF.

The value of a capacitor, if not printed on the capacitor in full, is usually indicated by a 3-digit code. The first 2 digits represent the first 2 digits of the value, in picofarads. The third digit indicates the number of zeroes following the two digits. For example, the code '223' indicates 22000pF = 22nF. A terminal letter indicates tolerance: J = ±5%; K = ±10%; M = ±20%; Z = −20% and +80%.

Capacitor values

Fixed capacitors of close tolerance, such as silvered mica capacitors, are manufactured in a series of values corresponding to those of the E12 resistor values:

10   12   15   18   22   27   33   39   47   56   68   82

The series repeats in higher decades (100, 120, etc.) and in lower decades (1.0, 1.2, etc.). Most types of capacitor are manufactured to lower tolerance so only 6 of these values are obtainable:

10   15   22   27   33   47   68

Electrolytic capacitors, which have very low tolerance, are usually available in only the 3 values 10, 22 and 47, in each decade.

Capacitor colour code

Colour codes are used far less often for capacitors than for resistors, but some types of polyester capacitor have coloured bands to indicate the capacitance in picofarads. There are three bands, two for the digits, the third as a multiplier.

Features of different types of fixed capacitor

Most types of capacitor, except for electrolytic and tantalum types, have high insulation resistance ($10G\Omega$ or more) and are intended to operate in the temperature range $-55°C$ to $100°C$. Aluminium electrolytic capacitors typically have a leakage current of $0.01 \times CV$, where the current is in μA, C is the capacity in μF and V is the working voltage; there is usually a minimum leakage current of between 2 and 3 μA. Leakage current drops to about 10% if the capacitor is operated at around 40% of its maximum working voltage, so this is a way of obtaining lower leakage. Tantalum capacitors have similar leakage currents, though the minimum is usually $1\mu A$. Since both aluminium electrolytics and tantalum capacitors are polarised, they are generally unsuitable for use with reverse voltages. Aluminium electrolytics must never be operated in such conditions, but tantalum can withstand low reverse voltages.

The characteristics of monolithic ceramic capacitors depend very much on the type of dielectric used. They are sometimes classified according to the permittivity (K) of the dielectric. High K capacitors have high capacitance for a given physical size indicated by the abbreviations X7R, (high K), 2F4, NPO and COG in Table 2. Those with XR7 have an operating range extending up to $125°C$.

Low K subminiature ceramic plate capacitors are made with a range of specified negative tempcos (0 to -4700 ppm/°C) for temperature compensation in tuning and similar circuits. The tempco is often indicated by the colour of the tip of the capacitor. For example: black = zero, orange = -150, violet = -750, blue/orange = -4700.

Working voltages are given for direct current. For alternating current the rating should be reduced, especially at radio frequencies. Voltage rating should also be reduced for pulse signals. Polystyrene capacitors are rated only from $-40°$ to

70°C, and high K plate ceramics only from −10° to 55°C.

The dissipation factor (tan δ), which in low-loss components is roughly equivalent to the power loss factor, is a measure of the ability of the dielectric to absorb energy, thus leading to a damping of a.c. signals and loss of power. It also reduces the sharpness of cut-off in filters. It is often frequency-dependent, usually being greater at high frequencies but, in mica, it is greater at low frequencies.

The codes used in the table below have the following meanings:

Range available
H = high range, 1µF or more
M = medium range, from about 1nF to about 1µF
L = low range, from about 2.2pF to 10nF

Tolerance − given as a percentage

Working voltage
H = 1000V d.c. or more
M = 250V − 600V d.c.
L = less than 250V d.c.

Tempco
H = 75 ppm/°C or more
L = less than 75 ppm/°C

Dissipation factor/power factor
H = DF > 0.5%
L = DF < 0.5%

Price
H = more than 20p per capacitor; with certain types, prices are considerably higher at the upper end of the capacitance range
L = 20p or less per capacitor over all or most of the range.

Table 2 is based on typical specifications. Types made by different manufacturers may vary in one or more particulars from the descriptions in the table. Several types, including

22

Table 2 – FEATURES OF FIXED CAPACITORS

Type	Range	Tolerance	Working voltage	Tempco	Dissipation factor/power factor	Price
Silvered mica	L	1	M	L	L	H
Ceramic – monolithic X7R	M	5, 10, 20	L	H	H	L
Ceramic – monolithic 2F4	M	–20 +80	L	H	H	H
Ceramic – monolithic NPO/COG	L	2, 5, 10	L	L^A	L	L
Ceramic – disc	M	–20 +80	H*	–	–	L
Ceramic – submin plate low K	L	2	L	**	L	L
Ceramic – submin plate med K	M	10	L	–	H	L
Ceramic – submin plate high K	M	–20 +80	L	–	H	L
Polypropylene	M	5, 10, 20	H	L	L	H
Polypropylene – miniature	L	5	L	L	L	H
Polycarbonate – miniature	L	10, 20	L	L	L	L
Polycarbonate – high volts	M	10, 20	H	L	H	H
Polycarbonate – brass case	M	5	L	L	L	H
Polyester	M	5, 10, 20	L or M	H	L	L to H
Polystyrene	L	1, 2, 5, 10	L to H	H	L	L
Polystyrene – precision	L	1	M	L	L	L
Aluminium electrolytic	H	20	L or M	–	H^B	L to H
Solid tantalum	H	20	L	–	H^B	H

* low voltage types available for logic circuits
** specified tempco

A – zero tempco
B – lower than for aluminium electrolytics

23

ceramic, silvered mica, polyester, aluminium electrolytic and tantalum capacitors are available for surface mounting.

Selecting a capacitor

Figure 4 is a flowchart for selecting capacitors on the basis of value required, tolerance, working voltage, physical size, tempco, and application. As different makes of capacitor may vary in their specification from the typical capacitors on which the flowchart is based, it is as well to confirm the selection by referring to a catalogue or to the manufacturer's data sheet. The chart does not include specialised capacitors such as those intended for use with motors or for computer memory back-up.

Polyester capacitors are often marked at one end to indicate which lead wire is connected to the outer foil. It is this lead which should be connected to 'Earth' in tuned circuits, to shield the capacitor from electromagnetic interference.

Capacitors in series

When two or more capacitors are joined in series, their combined capacitance is given by:

$$\frac{1}{C_T} = \frac{1}{C_1} + \frac{1}{C_2} + \frac{1}{C_3} + \ldots + \frac{1}{C_n}$$

For two capacitors in series, this formula can be simplified to:

$$C_T = \frac{C_1 \times C_2}{C_1 + C_2}$$

If two capacitors of the same type and value are connected in series, the total capacitance is halved. The tolerance remains unaltered.

Capacitors in parallel

When two or more capacitors are joined in parallel, their combined capacitance is given by:

$$C_T = C_1 + C_2 + C_3 + \ldots + C_n$$

For two capacitors of the same type and value connected in parallel, the total capacitance is doubled, and the tolerance is the same as each individual capacitor.

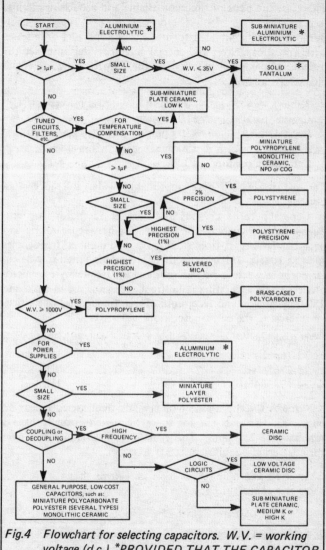

Fig.4 Flowchart for selecting capacitors. W.V. = working
voltage (d.c.) *PROVIDED THAT THE CAPACITOR
IS NOT SUBJECTED TO REVERSE VOLTAGES

3 Crystals and ceramic resonators

These are the basis of precision timing and oscillating circuits (see pages 218 to 219). The crystals are of 3 types, general-purpose crystals intended for use either in parallel or in series with a load capacitor, and special plug-in crystals intended for use in radio-control circuits on the 27MHz band. Typical characteristics are:

Type	Tolerance	Tempco (ppm/°C)
Crystal, parallel	±10−50ppm	12.5 − 200
Crystal, series	±50 ppm	12.5 − 200
27MHz	±30 ppm	−
Ceramic resonator	±0.5%	50

Ceramic resonators have appreciably wider tolerance than crystals.

General-purpose crystals and ceramic resonators are produced for a wide range of frequencies between 100kHz and over 20MHz. Apart from standard 'round number' frequencies such as 10kHz, 1MHz, etc., there are others suited to particular purposes such as providing the clock frequency for microprocessors or generating radio-frequencies for use in radio and TV transmission and reception. Three frequencies of particular interest to the constructor are:

Frequency	Divide by	Resultant frequency
32.768kHz	2^{15}	1Hz
3.2768MHz	2^{16}	50Hz
4.194304MHz	2^{22}	1Hz

Circuits for the division of crystals frequencies appear on page 243. Crystals cut for these frequencies usually have a tolerance of ±10 ppm. This table gives the timing error over various periods, equivalent to 10 ppm:

Period	Error
minute	6×10^{-4} s
hour	0.04s
day	0.86s
week	6.0s
month	26s
year	315s = 5mins

4 Inductors

This section covers all inductive components used for tuning, filtering, coupling, choking and the suppression of interference. Microphone and audio transformers are described on pages 147–149. Transformers used for power supplies are not dealt with in this book.

More than for most other types of component, suppliers differ widely in the range of inductors stocked. Some stock a few popular kinds while others stock hundreds. If you fail to find what you need in the catalogue of one supplier, try another.

Types of inductor

(i) **Chokes** for filtering or for the suppression of unwanted signals. These are wound on high-loss ferrite materials. They are subdivided into audio-frequency chokes with high inductance ($>1H$) and radio-frequency chokes with relatively low inductance ($0.22\mu H$ to $1mH$). Multiple chokes are available ready-connected for use as filters.

(ii) **Tuning coils** for radio frequencies ($>100kHz$). These are wound on a plastic former, with a threaded ferrite or iron dust core which may be adjusted using a special trimming tool. Such coils must be mechanically stable so that they are not put out of alignment by shock or by temperature extremes. Since they carry only small currents, saturation of the core is not a significant factor. This category includes inductors with two or more coils wound on the same former, as used in certain oscillators and as high-frequency transformers in radio and TV circuits.

(iii) **Energy-storage inductors** for use in power supplies. Stability is not important but they must be able to reach a high saturation flux density; the core often has a gap to increase saturation levels, or is made from iron dust which in effect has air gaps within the core. These include coils wound on ferrite toroids, intended to carry high currents.

Ready-wound inductors

When selecting a coil the following points need to be taken into account:

Self-inductance (L): This can range from $1\mu H$ up to about 1.5H.

Quality factor (Q): This is a measure of the selectivity of the inductor — the sharpness of its response to signals at a quoted test frequency. The larger the value of Q, the better the coil. Typically values range from 20 to 100. Q is greater at higher frequencies and in coils with higher inductance. To obtain high Q at relatively low (i.e. audio) frequencies, a coil wound on a pot core is usually recommended.

Maximum rated current: Exceeding this current may lead to fusion of the coil.

Temperature coefficient: This is not often quoted but is usually $100 - 200$ ppm/$^\circ$C, though it can be more.

Screening: A can screens the coil from external magnetic fields and also prevents the magnetic field of the coil from causing interference with other parts of the circuit.

Other features such as tunable frequency range, stability, DC resistance are usually quoted in the catalogues where they may be of interest to the designer.

Winding inductors

In spite of the wide range of inductors obtainable, it may still be necessary to wind one to fit a specific situation. The parts required for winding inductors are available individually: plastic formers, iron dust cores, pot cores, ferrite rods, toroids, and enamelled copper wire in various gauges.

(i) Single-layer coil, with air core: The length of the coil ℓ is 10 or more times greater than its radius r. The number of turns required is:

$$N = 5/r \times \sqrt{L(10\ell + 9r)}$$

where r and ℓ are in mm and L is in μH.

Example: to wind a coil length 40mm, radius 4mm, with self-inductance $10\mu H$, the number of turns required is $5/4 \times \sqrt{10(10 \times 40 + 9 \times 4)} = 1.25 \times \sqrt{(10 \times 436)} = 1.25 \times \sqrt{4360} = 82.5$ turns. Use enamelled copper wire for the coil. The thicker the wire, the lower the coil d.c. resistance and the higher the Q.

(ii) Multi-layer coil, with air core: The length of the coil is 2 or more times the radius. The mean radius of the windings is r, and the depth of the winding is d. The number of turns required is:

$$N = 15.8/r \times \sqrt{(Ld)}$$

where r and d are in mm and L is in μH.

Example: to wind a coil length 25mm, radius 10mm, depth 2mm, self-inductance 30μH, the number of turns required is $15.8/10 \times \sqrt{(30 \times 2)} = 1.58 \times \sqrt{60} = 12$ turns. See the remarks above about wire thickness. To wind an air-cored coil with inductance greater than about 100mH requires too many turns for convenience, in which case a ferrite or iron dust core must be used (see below).

The above formulae are approximate and it is not always easy to prepare the coil to exactly the specified dimensions. The inductance is measured by using an inductance bridge, if available, or by connecting the inductor in parallel with a known capacitor and using a frequency generator and oscilloscope to determine the resonant frequency, f_0. Then $L = 1/(4\pi^2 f_0^2 C)$.

If it is found that the finished coil does not have the required inductance, the inductance may be adjusted by adding or removing turns. If L is the required inductance and L_A is the actual inductance of a coil with N_A turns, the required number of turns N is given by:

$$N = N_A \sqrt{(L/L_A)}$$

(iii) **Using a plastic former and iron dust core:** Calculations may be made as above, taking into account the fact that the presence of the dust core will increase the inductance by about 2 to 5 times. See the remarks above about wire thickness. Wind the coil on the former, not directly on the core, as the former keeps the coil away from the core and so reduces the self-capacitance of the inductor. If possible wind in a single layer, to keep self-capacitance low but, if this is not possible, wind the coil irregularly, or use a multi-section former and wind the coil in two or more sections on the same core.

Two or more coils may be wound on the same core to produce transformers for radio circuits.

(iv) Using a pot core: Manufacturers usually quote the *inductance factor* or *specific inductance* of the core, A_L, which is the inductance per turn squared. This makes the calculations simpler, for the number of turns required is:

$$N = \sqrt{(L/A_L)}$$

Example: a core has $A_L = 250\text{nH/turn}^2$. To wind a 150mH coil, we calculate:

$$N = \sqrt{((150 \times 10^{-3})/(250 \times 10^{-9}))} = \sqrt{600000} = 775 \text{ turns}$$

See the remarks above about wire thickness, noting that if the wire is too thick, it may not be possible to wind the full number of turns on the bobbin.

With a pot core the magnetic field is more-or-less confined to the core and screening is usually not necessary.

(v) Using a toroid: Toroids provide a simple way to produce high-frequency chokes and transformers to a required value. The magnetic field is confined to the core and screening is unnecessary. Toroids are made from a number of different 'mixes', each with its own characteristic permeability and suited to a particular range of resonant frequencies. Manufacturers' data tables list toroids of a range of sizes and 'mixes' and quote the inductance, often that for a 100-turn coil. The number of turns required for coils of other inductance values can be calculated as in section (ii) above. The tables also indicate which gauge of wire should be used for winding.

(vi) Ferrite beads: These may be slipped on to the wires to act as high-frequency chokes. They are particularly useful in suppressing transients on power supply lines. For example, the 555 timer ic (page 224) produces serious spikes which can affect other components in the same circuit. These spikes can be damped out by threading the power lines to the ic through one or two ferrite beads.

5 Diodes

Very many types of diode are available, so that it is not possible to give firm guidelines to the best diode for any given application. In this section, a selection has been made from the more popular and less expensive types, which will work reasonably well in most applications. For critical situations, consult the manufacturer's or supplier's data tables.

There are two main categories of diode, germanium diodes and silicon diodes, of which the silicon diode is by far the most commonly used. Forward conduction in germanium diodes begins at approximately 0.2V. In silicon diodes it begins at about 0.6V. Germanium diodes generally have a larger reverse leakage current than silicon diodes. When subjected to the peak (maximum allowable) inverse voltage, or PIV, germanium diodes have a leakage current between 0.25 mA and 1mA. Silicon diodes have a leakage current of only a few tens of nanoamps; it is rather higher (about $10\mu A$) in high-power rectifier diodes.

When deciding on the wattage required, it is usually safe to take the forward voltage drop as 0.6V (for a silicon diode). Multiply this by the forward current to find the power dissipated. If the diode is carrying current near its rated maximum, take the forward voltage to be 1V, possibly more.

General purpose and signal diodes
For a wide range of applications including clamping, clipping, biassing, logic, op amp rectifiers, use the very inexpensive 1N4148, or its equivalent 1N914. These carry a forward current of up to 100mA, and have a PIV of 75V. A low capacitance version of the 1N914 is the 1N916. A general-purpose diode with higher ratings is the BY206 ($I_F = 400$ mA, PIV = 350V). For surface mount technology use the BAS16 ($I_F = 0.6A$, PIV = 85V) or the dual diode, the BAS28.

For a lower forward voltage drop (0.4V at 10mA) combined with extra-fast switching time, use a Schottky diode, such as the BAT42. The disadvantages of Schottky diodes are low PIV and higher reverse leakage.

If a germanium diode is preferred, use the OA91 or similar diode. For detection in radio circuits, the OA47 is a germanium diode with low V_F (0.4V at 10mA) and fast switching time.

Rectifier diodes

The most popular rectifier diodes are those of the 1N4000 and 1N5400 series, rated for maximum forward currents of 1A and 3A respectively. For use in switch mode power supplies the corresponding series are the UF4000 and UF5400 series with 50ns recovery time. The PIV for the 1N4000 series is indicated by the last digit of the type number: 1 = 50V, 2 = 100V, 3 = 200V, 4 = 400V, 5 = 600V, 6 = 800V, 7 = 1000V. For example, the 1N4006 has a PIV of 800V. In the 1N5400 series the corresponding figures are: 0 = 50V, 1 = 100V, 2 = 200V, 4 = 400V, 6 = 600V, 7 = 800V, 8 = 1000V. For example, the 1N5406 has a PIV of 600V.

Schottky barrier diodes such as the MBR150 and MBR350 are useful rectifiers where fast switching is important. They are rated at 1A and 3A respectively, and have low forward voltage drop (about 0.7V at maximum forward current, compared with 1.1V for the 1N4000 and 1N5400 series). However, they are unable to withstand high reverse voltages (PIV = 50V). They are particularly suitable for high-current low-voltage supplies.

There are many other rectifier diodes for operation at higher voltages and higher currents than those quoted above. Stud-mounting types must be attached to heat sinks when operating at high power.

An alternative to using individual diodes is to use a bridge rectifier consisting of 4 such diodes already connected into a full-wave bridge (p.306). These are available in a range of ratings from 1A up to 60A, to withstand PIVs ranging from 200V to 1200V. Such bridges have holes for mounting them on heat sinks.

Zener diodes

These are available with a Zener voltage V_z ranging from 2.4V to 270V. Within the range, the values per decade are those of the E24 series, as used for resistors (p.10). The range may be restricted in some series, the lower or higher values being unavailable, or only the E12 values being provided. Tolerance is usually 5%.

The only other parameter of importance is the power rating. Calculate the power required by using the formula

$P = IV_z$, where I is the maximum current through the diode. Then select a diode from a range with the next greater power rating. Power ratings commonly available are:

Series	Power (W)
BZY88/BZX55	0.4
BZX79	0.5
BZX85/BZX61/ZPY100	1.3
1N5333	5
BZY93	20

The BZY93 series are in a stud-mounting package, for mounting on a heat sink.

Constant-current diodes
These are two-terminal devices consisting of an FET (p.34) with the source connected internally to the gate. The current passed by the device is constant when it is forward biased with a voltage exceeding $1.7 - 4.2$V (dependent on type) but not exceeding 50V. Types are available for currents between 0.56mA and 4.7mA (20% tolerance).

Varicap diodes
A useful varicap for AM tuning is the BB212. Its capacitance varies from about 560pF to 22pF, more-or-less linearly as the reverse voltage ranges from 0.5V to 8V. Other types are available suitable for VHF and UHF tuning. Also there are dual and triple diodes on the same chip to ensure uniform temperature for ganged tuning.

For **light-emitting diodes**, see p.266. For **photodiodes**, see p.55. In all the diodes mentioned in this section, the cathode terminal is indicated by a band marked on the body of the device.

6 Transistors
The remarks given at the beginning of the Section 5 also apply to the suggestions made in this section.

Junction bipolar transistors
These are subdivided into *npn* and *pnp* types. In the selection

table below, *npn* and *pnp* transistors listed on the same line are complementary. The BC547 to BC559 are the plastic package equivalents of the BC107 to BC179 transistors. f_T is the *transition frequency*, the frequency at which the gain of the transistor falls to 1, when connected in the common emitter configuration (p.92). The maximum gain at a lower frequency f can be calculated as f_T/f, limited by the quoted low frequency gain, h_{fe}. Surface mounting equivalents are given in brackets – see Table 3.

The terminal connections of these transistors are illustrated in Figure 5.

Junction field effect transistors (JFETs)
Compared with junction bipolar transistors, JFETs offer the advantage of high input impedance, there being virtually no current flowing to the gate. Thus their response is controlled by *voltage*, not by *current*, as in the case of the bipolar transistors. JFETs suffer from the disadvantages that individual transistors vary widely in the values of their characteristics; in particular, the pinch-off voltage (the threshold V_{GS}) may vary three-fold, making the transistor difficult to bias accurately. The saturated drain current I_{DSS} may vary ten-fold.

JFETs are subdivided into *n*-channel and *p*-channel types. All the types listed in Table 4 operate in the depletion mode (i.e. conduction occurs when there is zero gate voltage). Transistors listed on the same line are similar but not necessarily complementary. Several (including the 2N3819) are available as surface mount transistors.

The terminal connections of these transistors are illustrated in Figure 6.

Metal oxide semiconductor field effect transistors (MOSFETs)
MOSFETs offer the same advantage as JFETs, of having a high input impedance. The constructions of certain types of MOSFET (particularly VMOS transistors) allows for high power ratings, and makes them ideal for power switching from very small current sources (e.g. CMOS gate outputs). MOS-FETs generally have a higher gain (transconductance) than JFETs, ranging from 100 to 20000mS, compared with a range of 1 to 10mS for JFETs. They have good thermal stability,

Table 3 – JUNCTION BIPOLAR TRANSISTORS

Power	Frequency (and applications)	npn	pnp
LOW (small signal) <0.5W	LOW (general purpose and audio amplifiers) $f_T \leq 300\text{MHz}$	BC107A (BCW72) BC108* (BCW31) BC109*+ (BCF33) BC547* BC548* BC549*+ ZTX300B (BCW60) 2SC2547E*++	BC177A BC178* BC179*+ BC557* BC558* (BCW30) BC559*+ ZTX500B 2SA1085E*++
	HIGH (r.f. amplifiers and tuners) $f_T > 300\text{MHz}$	BF173 BF180C 2N2222AD (BSR14)	
MEDIUM 0.5W to 15W	LOW (audio amplifiers) $f_T \leq 300\text{MHz}$	BC140 ZTX650E BD131F	BC160 ZTX750E BD132F
	HIGH (HF/VHF driver) $f_T > 300\text{MHz}$	2N3866	
HIGH >15W	(output stages of audio amps, power control)	TIP3055 2N3055	TIP2955 2N2955
DARLINGTON pairs, low power low power, high volts high power high power, high volts		MPSA14* (BCV27) MPSA42* MJ3001* MJ11016*	MPSA65* MPSA92* MJ2501* MJ11015*
HIGH VOLTAGE ($V_{CEO} = \pm150\text{V}$)		2N5551	2N5401

* indicates a high gain transistor ($h_{FE} > 300$). Medium and high power transistors usually have lower gain (<100) than low power transistors.

\+ indicates a low noise transistor, and ++ indicates very low noise.

A higher voltage rating (than BC108, BC109, etc.).

B maximum current 500mA (compared with 100mA for BC transistors in this group).

C slightly lower power (150mW) but much higher frequency than BF173; for UHF amplifiers and tuners.

D maximum current 600mA; high speed switching.

E double power rating (2A) and slightly higher gain (200) than BC140/160.

F higher power (15W) but lower gain and frequency than others in this group; available as matched pairs; audio output stages.

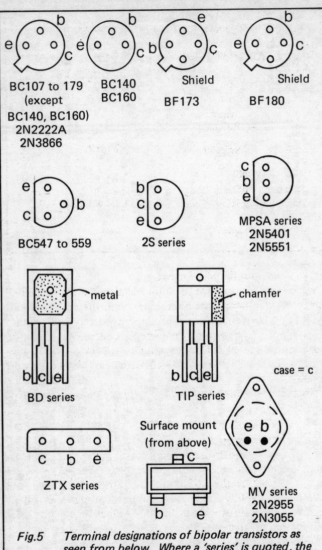

Fig.5 Terminal designations of bipolar transistors as seen from below. Where a 'series' is quoted, the designation applies to all transistors listed in the table, but not necessarily to non-listed transistors

36

Table 4 – JUNCTION FIELD EFFECT TRANSISTORS

Power	Applications	n-channel	p-channel
LOW (small signal) <0.5W	General purpose and a.f. amplifiers	2N3819* 2N5457A	2N3820 2N5460A
	Switching R.f. amplifiers	J112 J310**	J175
MEDIUM	Switching	2N4393B	

* high gain (4mS)

** high gain (8mS)

A higher power (310mW) compared with 200mW for 2N3819 and 2N3820

B power rating 1.8W.

and freedom from thermal runaway.

MOSFETs are subdivided into *n*-channel and *p*-channel types. All transistors listed here operate in the enhancement mode (i.e. there is no conduction at zero gate voltage). Transistors listed on the same line are complementary. Those specifically intended for logic switching are indicated in the selection Table 5. Several are available as surface mount transistors.

The terminal connections of these transistors are illustrated in Figure 7.

Unijunction transistors

This type of transistor is mainly used in circuits such as timers, oscillators, and ramp generators. The type most commonly used is the 2N2646. Two other transistors, the BRY39 and 2N6027 can be programmed, using 2 resistors, as unijunction transistors with specified values for the intrinsic stand-off radio, base-to-base resistance, peak current and valley-point current. They can also be programmed as silicon controlled switches and thyristor tetrodes. Terminal connections are illustrated in Figure 8.

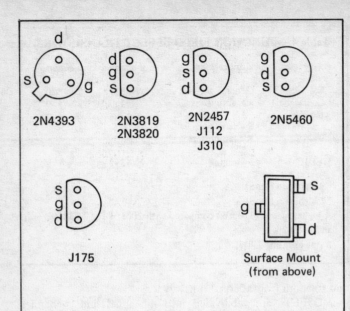

Fig.6   Terminal designations of JFETs (from below)

Transistor arrays

Several transistors in a single d.i.l. package offer advantages in pcb space saving and often some simplification in the layout. They are also valuable where thermal matching is important. Arrays available include:

Type	Transistor array	Applications
CA3046	5 × *npn*, incl. 2 with common emitters	general purpose
CA3083	5 × *npn*, high current (100mA)	switching, relay and display driving
SSM2210	2 × *npn*	low noise, matched audio pair
TPQ6502	2 × *npn*, 2 × *pnp*, complementary transistors	thermal matching
VQ1000J	4 × *n*-channel enhancement mode power MOSFETs (0.3A each)	logic level input

Table 5 – MOSFETs

Power	Application	n-channel	p-channel
LOW (small signal) <1W		ZVN3306A ZVN4206A[A]	ZVP2126A
MEDIUM 1W	Logic switching	VN10KM RFL1N20L	
HIGH >1W		IRF510	IRF9620
		VN46AF VN66AF[B]	
		2SK135	2SJ50
	Logic switching	RFP12N10L	
FETLINGTON pair		2N7000[C]	

A about double the power rating (600mA) and double the gain (300mS) of the ZVN3306A, lower ON resistance (1.5Ω compared with 5Ω) but higher V_{GS} threshold (3V compared with 2.4V).
B higher gain than VN46AF (195mS compared with 150mS) but higher V_{DS} threshold (2.5V compared with 1.7V).
C can pass a continuous current of 200mA: ON resistance = 2.4Ω

Thyristors, triacs and diacs

The main consideration when choosing a thyristor or silicon controlled rectifier is its power rating. If the thyristor is to be used to switch alternating current, another important characteristic is the peak inverse voltage. A very large number of different types is available but they nearly all fall into one of three categories:

Low power, low PIV: for example the BRY55-100, with forward current (r.m.s.) up to 0.8A, and PIV100V. The BRY39 (see unijunction transistors in previous section) also comes into this category. Applications include any low voltage low current triggering circuit, displaying driving, relay driving. Note that the forward voltage drop can be up to 2V.

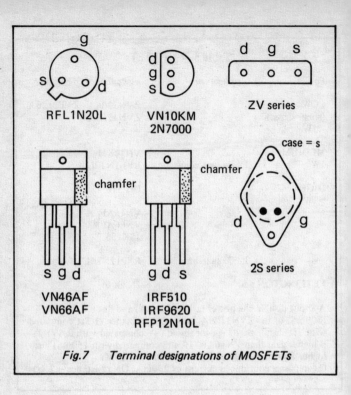

Fig.7   Terminal designations of MOSFETs

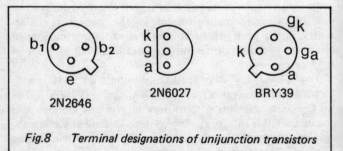

Fig.8   Terminal designations of unijunction transistors

Medium power, high PIV: one of the most often used is the C106D, with forward current (r.m.s.) up to 4A, and PIV 400V. Suitable for controlling AC mains supplies to lamps, bells and small motors.

High power, high PIV: a wide range is available for currents up to 110A and PIV up to 1200V. For switching multiple lamps, heaters, heavy-duty motors.

A thyristor is triggered by a positive pulse to its gate. The firing circuit must provide a pulse of sufficient voltage V_{GT} and provide sufficient current I_{GT} to initiate conduction. V_{GT} is usually between 0.8V and 2.5V, the larger values of V_{GT} being associated with thyristors of higher rating. Equally important is the fact that the firing circuit must be capable of providing at least the minimum I_{GT}. With lower-power thyristors I_{GT} is less than 1mA, but with those of higher power rating as much as 100mA may be required. It is also important for the triggering pulse to have a rapid rise time, otherwise the thyristor is turned on slowly and excessive power is dissipated in the thyristor while it is being turned on.

Greater efficiency is obtainable by using a triac, a bi-directional thyristor. These are obtainable in the same three categories as thyristors. They are triggered by both positive and negative pulses; the remarks of the previous paragraph apply to triacs too. Triac circuits usually make use of a bi-directional trigger diode, a diac, to fire the triac. Most available diacs have similar properties, with a breakover (triggering) voltage of 32V. Once this voltage has been reached the diac conducts freely.

A device related to the thyristor is the gate turn-off switch. This has three terminals (anode, cathode and gate) and like a thyristor, allows only one-way conduction. The difference is that the device is turned on by a positive pulse to the gate and is turned off by a negative pulse. An example is the BTW58-1300R, which is rated at 6.5A.

The construction of power-control circuits presents possible safety hazards, especially to the less experienced constructor. Some of the problems may be minimised or avoided by making use of ready-assembled totally enclosed units.

8 Voltage references

These are often referred to as *band-gap references*. There are two kinds, the 2-terminal references and the multi-terminal references. The 2-terminal references are usually connected into a circuit in the same way as a Zener diode. There are available in a number of standard voltages, ranging from 1.2V to about 10V; this range is much more restricted than that of Zener diodes but the tolerance is much closer (1% or better) and tempco is much less (less than 100 ppm/°C, often as little as 30 ppm). A certain minimum current I_{REF} is required to produce the reference voltage, and for most devices this must be in the range 50µA to 5mA. A reference resistor (Fig.9) is selected to provide this, using the formula:

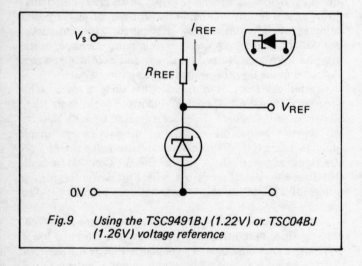

Fig.9   Using the TSC9491BJ (1.22V) or TSC04BJ
         (1.26V) voltage reference

$$R_{REF} = \frac{V_S - V_{REF}}{I_{REF}}$$

where V_S is the supply voltage. References of this type include the MP5010GN (1.22V), REF25Z (2.5V) and REF50Z (5.0V). The ZN423 (1.26V) and ZN458B (2.45V) are similar but with higher minimum and maximum reference currents.

42

Multi-terminal references are either programmable over a given range (2.5V to 10V, for example) or can be trimmed to give an output within a few percent of their nominal value. Thus the ZNREF025, with a nominal output of 2.5V (1% tolerance) can be trimmed to give an output of 2.56V, providing a useful reference voltage for an 8-bit analogue-to-digital converter. The LM3999 is a Zener diode package with a heater to compensate for temperature variations. It has a reverse voltage of 6.95V (5% tolerance) and operates with a supply voltage in the range 9V to 36V. I_{REF} may range from $600\mu A$ to 10mA; its tempco is only 2 ppm/$^\circ$C.

9 Constant current devices

By using a single resistor (Fig.10), a device such as the LM334Z can be used as a constant current generator. Current can range from $1\mu A$ to 10mA. The current is proportional to the kelvin temperature. This gives the device an application as a temperature sensor but, by using the circuit in Figure 10b, the tempco can be adjusted to zero.

10 Operational amplifiers

A very wide range is available, of which a few representative ones are listed below, Figure 11 shows pinout connections. Transconductance operational amplifiers are described in Section 11, p.48. The main points to consider when selecting an op amp are:

Supply voltage range: Some operate only on a double supply (positive and negative rails); these are usually saturated by input voltages within a few volts of the supply rails. Others are able to accept an input voltage as low as the most negative rail and so operate on a single supply. Such types are usually saturated by input voltages within a volt or two of the most positive rail. The minimum supply voltage can be as low as 2V ($\pm$1V), the maximum as high as 40V ($\pm$20V), depending on type.

Supply current: Low power consumption is important for battery-powered circuits. Several of the CMOS op amps require only $10\mu A$ when quiescent.

Output voltage swing: For some types the output swings very close to both supply rails but, in most types, it swings

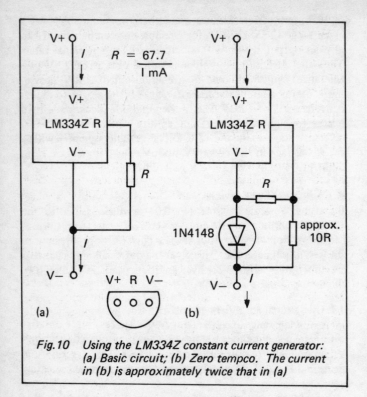

Fig.10 Using the LM334Z constant current generator:
(a) Basic circuit; (b) Zero tempco. The current
in (b) is approximately twice that in (a)

no closer than 2V, e.g. a swing of ±13V when operated at
±15V.

Input bias current: The amount of current required to bias
the input stages into correct operating conditions. This is
usually a few nanoamps in bipolar op amps. In JFET and
CMOS op amps there is no bias current as such but there are
usually a few picoamps of leakage current.

Input offset voltage: The difference of input voltages
required to produce zero output voltage. Precision op amps
have offsets of 200μV or less. Some op amps have terminals
by which an external circuit is used to compensate for offset,
see Figures 12 and 13. Packages with more than one amplifier usually do not. Input offset compensation is rarely

required in a.c. signal circuits.

Slew rate: A high slew rate is needed for high-frequency operation. A normal slew rate is in the order of $1-10V/\mu s$, typical for both bipolar and CMOS op amps. JFET op amps generally have rates greater than $10V/\mu s$, the highest-frequency op amps having rates up to $600V/\mu s$.

Gain-bandwidth product: In all op amps the gain falls off with increasing frequency. Typically, gain falls regularly above 10kHz (the *full-power bandwidth*) until it reaches unity (1) at 1MHz. Such an amplifier is said to have a gain-bandwidth product of 1MHz. This value can be used to calculate the approximate gain at other frequencies. With a GBP of 1MHz, the gain is 2 at 500kHz, 10 at 100kHz, 200 at 5kHz, and so on. High-frequency op amps with GBPs of several hundred megahertz are available.

Common mode rejection ratio: Differences in the gain of the two inputs may lead to any signal which is present equally on *both* inputs appearing at the output. Noise is an example of such a signal. CMMR is expressed in decibels (p.6), the ratio involved being the differential open-loop voltage gain (inputs not joined together) divided by the common mode open-loop voltage gain (inputs joined together).

Other characteristics that are sometimes important are: drift (variation of output with time and with temperature changes), external frequency compensation facilities, settling time.

Two points that do not usually require consideration are:

Input impedance: although the input impedance of the op amp is very high ($2M\Omega$ or considerably more), this is not of general importance because the input impedance of the *circuit* in which the op amp is used is usually determined by resistors of values much lower than this.

Output impedance: this is generally in the region of 75Ω. For an increased supply of current, an external transistor can be used, as shown on p.167.

Open loop voltage gain: this is in the region of 200,000 for most op amps and, in any case, the final gain of the *circuit* is fixed at a value *much* lower than this by the feedback and other resistors.

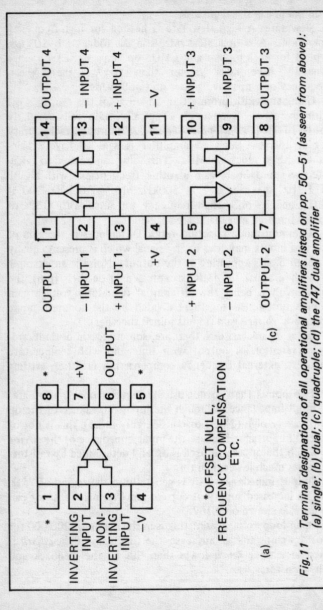

Fig.11   Terminal designations of all operational amplifiers listed on pp. 50–51 (as seen from above):
(a) single; (b) dual; (c) quadruple; (d) the 747 dual amplifier

46

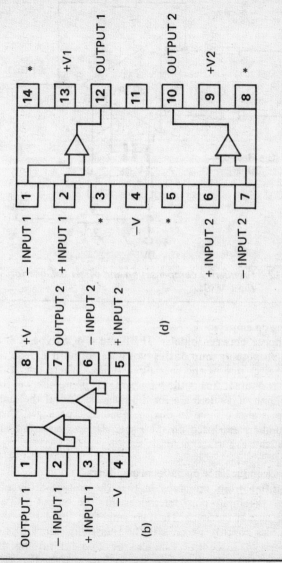

Fig.11 Continued

47

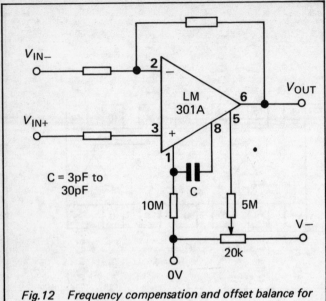

Fig.12   Frequency compensation and offset balance for the LM301A

Selecting op amps

First choose between bipolar, JFET and CMOS types. If a general purpose op amp of this type does not fulfil all requirements, select one of the specialised types. Where operating voltage is quoted, this is the *minimum*. Type numbers in the first column of Table 6 are for the single version; if the same op amp is also offered in dual or quadruple packages, their type numbers are listed on the right. Devices marked * are also available as surface mount ic's.

11 Transconductance operational amplifiers

These differ from op amps in that the voltage difference between the input pins determines not the output voltage but the output *current*. The two amplifiers listed here also have a bias control, which sets the transconductance of the amplifier. This control can also be used for turning the output on and off. It should always have a 100kΩ resistor

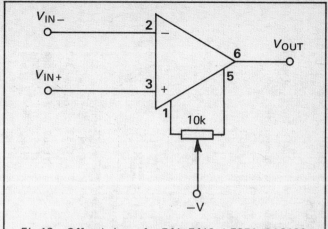

Fig.13 Offset balance for 741, 741S, LF351, CA3130,
CA3140. Reference to +V for LF355 and
ICL7611. Use 100k potentiometer for TL061,
TL071, TL081. Reference to 0V for TLC251

wired in series with it.

The CA3080 (single amplifier) and the LM13700N (dual amplifier) both have low minimum supply voltage (± 2V) high slew rate, unity gain bandwidth of 2MHz, input resistance 26kΩ (lower than ordinary op amps), transconductance 9600mS, and peak output current 500μA. The LM13700 has, in addition, linearising input diodes (to reduce distortion and to help protect against overloading the inputs) and two buffers (Darlington pairs) to increase output current. Figure 14 shows pinout details.

12 Comparators

Operational amplifiers can be used as comparators but better performance is obtained from ic's specifically designed for the purpose. The main advantage of the comparator is that it has high slew rate, and its output is usually designed to make it logic compatible. Figure 15 shows pinout details.

Table 6 – SELECTING OP AMPS

Type	Features	Dual	Quadruple
Bipolar op amps: usually have the lowest offset voltages, easy to handle, some are very inexpensive.			
LM301A	low input offset (but lower gain, low slew rate), external frequency compensation	—	—
LM308	low drift, low input offset current (0.2nA), low supply current (0.3mA), high input resistance (40MΩ)	—	—
—	single supply, 3V or ±1.5V operation		LM324N
—	single supply, 3V operation, low operating current (500µA)	LM358	—
NE531	high slew rate (35V/µs), external frequency compensation	—	—
OP-07CN	high precision, low input bias current (±2.2nA), high input resistance (33MΩ)	—	—
OP-90GP	low supply voltage, single supply, low power (20µA)		OP490GP
741*	cheap general purpose op amp	747	LM348N
741S	high-speed version of 741 (slew rate = 20V/µs, compared with 0.5V/µs), and with wider bandwidth (up to 100kHz at full power)		
JFET op amps: very high input impedance, very low input bias current, low input offset voltage.			
AD711	high speed, low offset, low drift, low noise	AD712	
LF351+	high slew rate (13V/µs)	LF353	LF347
LF355	low input offset voltage	—	—
TL061	low power (but lower slew rate), low supply voltage (±2V)	TL062	TL064*
TL071	low noise, low supply voltage (±2V)	TL072*	TL074*
TL081*	general purpose, low supply voltage (±2V)	TL082	TL084*

Type	Features	Dual	Quadruple
CMOS op amps: very high input impedance, low supply voltage, wide CMMR, usually wide voltage swings, but low slew rate.			
CA3130E*	output swings to both rails, single supply, wide bandwidth (15MHz)	—	—
CA3140E*	low supply voltage (±2V, 4V) single supply	CA3240	—
CA3160E	can accept inputs 0.5V *below* negative rail – good for single supply operation	CA3260	—
ICL7611*A	low operating voltage (±1V), low power (10µW) *or* wide bandwidth (1.6MHz) programmable, output swings to both rails	ICL7621*	ICL7641
			ICL7642
TLC251*B	low operating voltage (1V), low power, single supply, stable input offset voltage, programmable	—	—

+ inputs must never go below negative rail

A pin 8 to V+ gives supply current 10µA (ICL7642 is non-programmable version of this); pin 8 to 0V gives supply current 100µA; pin 8 to −V gives supply current 1mA, and high bandwidth (ICL7641 is non-programmable version of this).

B supply current and a.c. performance programmable; similar to ICL7611.

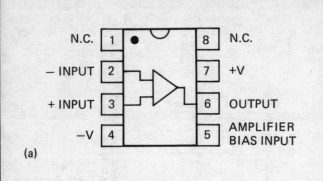

(a)

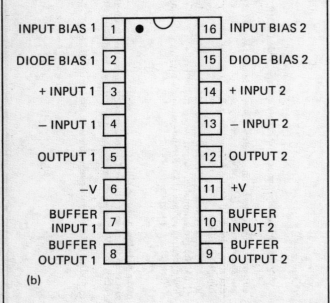

(b)

Fig.14   Terminal designations of transconductance
amplifiers, as seen from above: (a) CA3080; (b) LM13700N

52

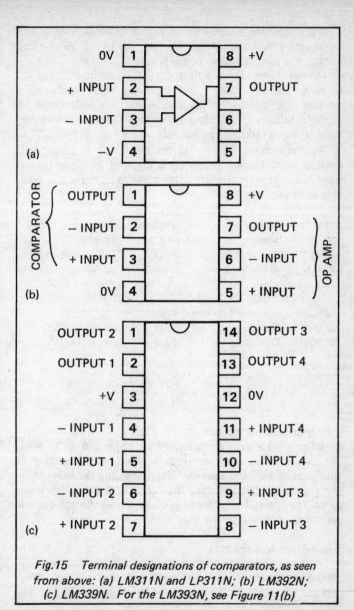

Fig.15 Terminal designations of comparators, as seen from above: (a) LM311N and LP311N; (b) LM392N; (c) LM339N. For the LM393N, see Figure 11(b)

53

When selecting a comparator, points to consider regarding input and power supply are the same as for op amps. For output, the main points to consider are:

Output type: Open-collector (O/C) output requires an external pull-up resistor; this type has wider applications because the resistor can be connected to a wide range of positive voltages. A totem-pole output requires no external resistor, but is rated to operate only on 5V.

● **Response time:** Usually in the range $0.2 - 2.5\mu s$. All devices listed below operate on a single or dual supply and have open-collector outputs. Devices marked * are also available as surface mount ic's.

Type	Package contains	Response time	Special features
LM311N*	Single comp	$0.2\mu s$	TTL compatible
LP311N	Single comp	$1.2\mu s$	TTL compatible; low power version of LM311N
LM392N*	1 comp + 1 op amp	$1.3\mu s$	
LM339N*	Quad comp	$1.3\mu s$	Low supply (2V)
LM393N	Dual comp	$1.3\mu s$	Low supply (2V)

13 Optoelectronic devices

Light-emitting diodes are described on pages 266–271. With the exception of the optocouplers, the devices described in this section are light sensors. When selecting the best sensor for a given application, take into account the required sensitivity, the spectral response (especially the wavelength of peak response) and the response time.

Light-dependent resistors

LDRs are also known as photoconductive cells and as photo-resistive cells, and are inexpensive and easy to use. Their resistance varies with the amount of light falling on them. The most popular LDR is the ORP12 which has the following response to light level:

Illumination	Resistance
Darkness	1MΩ (min.) − 10MΩ
10 lux	10kΩ
1000 lux	400Ω
10000 lux	80Ω (direct sunlight)

These figures show that the LDR is suitable for operation at all light levels, including very low ones. The cell responds to light in the wavebands 480nm (red) to 680nm (green) with peak response at 530nm (yellow). This response is reasonably close to that of the human eye, a point that makes the cell suitable for colour-matching applications. The overall colour temperature of the illumination affects response. In light of low colour temperature (reddish, e.g. from filament lamps or flames) resistances are lower than given above (down to about 50%). In light of high colour temperature (whitish/ bluish, e.g. midday sunlight, fluorescent lamps) resistances are up to double those listed above.

LDRs have the advantage that they can be operated with alternating current. Their main disadvantage is that their response time is much slower than that of other light sensors. The rise time (time for resistance to increase when light is cut off) is 18ms − 75ms, depending on circuit conditions. The fall time (time for resistance to decrease) is 120ms − 350ms. Note that these times are expressed in *milli*seconds, compared with times in nanoseconds for most other light sensors.

Photodiodes and photovoltaic cells

Photodiodes are generally used in the reverse-biased mode. The leakage current is linearly proportional to the amount of light falling on the diode. The linear response makes them suitable for photometry. Reverse current is typically only a few nano-amps in darkness but rises to 1mA or more in the light. The small current means that some form of amplification is required. Some have an amplifier built-in on the same chip. Photodiodes are available with a large exposed area (up to 100mm²) to give increased sensitivity. The peak sensitivity is usually toward the red end of the spectrum; some types are specifically designed as infra-red photodiodes. Others have a colour-filter over the sensitive area to produce a response approximating to that of the human eye.

Response time of photodiodes is fast, typically 250ns, and PIN photodiodes have even quicker response. For example, the BPX65 has a response time of only 0.5ns. Fast response time makes photodiodes suitable for high-speed counting and for use as modulated light detectors. For switching purposes, photodiodes are available with an integrated switching circuit on the same chip.

The photodiode is related to the *photovoltaic cell*, and certain types are specially designed to be usable in this way. A voltage is generated which is linearly proportional to the intensity of light falling on the cell. This voltage may be measured with a suitable circuit. In such circuits no biasing voltage is applied to the cell.

Photovoltaic cells intended for power generation, as opposed to being used as light sensors, are called *solar cells*. They are available individually and produce an e.m.f. of about 0.5V in bright sunlight. More often they are sold as an array ready connected in series to give 9V or more. Such arrays have a relatively low power output, often less than half a watt, since photovoltaic cells are not efficient as transducers. However they can provide enough power to drive a small motor. Even just one or two photovoltaic cells can provide power for simple electronic circuits, particularly those which make use of low-power devices such as CMOS operational amplifiers or logic.

Phototransistors
In these the incident light has the same action as the base current supplied to an ordinary *npn* transistor. Some types have a bias terminal but in others this is absent, there being only connections to the collector and emitter. The MEL12 phototransistor is a Darlington pair, with very high gain; this gives it a dark current of only 100nA, but a light current in the region of 3mA. Having the amplification inherent in the transistor action, phototransistors are more sensitive than photodiodes. Their disadvantage is that they have a slower response time. Response time may be reduced in those

phototransistors with a base connector by biasing the transistor with a small base current (typically $2\mu A$). To obtain rapid response time with high sensitivity it is better to use a photodiode with an integral amplifier.

Optocouplers and related devices
These are used for transferring signals from one circuit to another when there is a large voltage difference between the two circuits. This may be a matter of safety or to protect delicate components in the lower-voltage circuit. Optocouplers are also known as *optoisolators*, a name which gives prominence to their other main function of electrically isolating the two circuits. This can be of use if a direct electrical connection between two circuits would give rise to some undesirable situation, such as the formation of a ground loop (p.307). The optocoupler comprises a light-emitting diode sealed in a light-proof package with a photosensitive device. There may be several such LED/sensor pairs in the same package, each operating independently. The electrical insulation between the elements of the package is proof against potential differences of several thousand volts. The characteristics of the LED and photosensitive device are usually identical with those of the individually packaged equivalents, so no special criteria apply to designing for their use.

In the simplest optocouplers, variations in the input signal applied to the LED are transmitted to a phototransistor. The phototransistor is wired into the external circuit in the usual way and the coupled signal appears across it. For greater sensitivity (i.e. the ability to operate with a smaller input signal), the light-sensitive device is a photo-Darlington transistor. For higher operating speed the light from the LED is sensed by a photodiode, reverse-biased by the external circuit. Integrated with the photodiode are circuits to amplify the signal. The photodiode is sensitive to this light and a corresponding signal appears across it. For power control the optocoupler contains a photosensitive triac. A pulse of current through the LED is the equivalent of sending a triggering pulse to the gate of a normal triac.

14 Sensors

Light sensors have been described in the previous section.

Thermal sensors

(i) Thermistors: Thermistors are of two types, negative temperature coefficient (ntc) and positive temperature coefficient (ptc). The resistance of an ntc thermistor decreases as temperature increases, according to this relationship:

$$R_T = R_{ref}e^{\beta(1/T - 1/T_{ref})}$$

R_T is the resistance in ohms at a given temperature T, expressed in kelvin, R_{ref} is the resistance at a given reference temperature T_{ref}, usually 298K (25°C). The constant β depends on the material from which the thermistor is made. The constant e is the exponential constant, which has the value 2.718 to 3 decimal places. The relationship to temperature is not linear but the departure from linearity is not of practical significance over a limited range of temperature.

Negative tempco thermistors are available as bars, discs or small encapsulated beads. The latter form is suitable for measuring temperatures in confined spaces. They are available in a range of resistances from about 25Ω to 1MΩ, with a tolerance of 10% or 20%. The low tolerance means that the circuit must be designed with trimmer resistors to match the thermistor to the circuit parameters. However, special 'curve-matched thermistors' can be obtained with a tolerance of 0.2%. The maximum temperature measurable is usually 150° but special high-temperature thermistors have a range up to 450°C. One of the disadvantages of thermistors is self-heating. This results from the current that must necessarily be passed through a thermistor when measuring its resistance. The dissipation constant is the amount of power dissipated to produce a rise in temperature of 1°C above ambient. For most thermistors this is in the range 0.02 to 5mW/°C. Another practical feature of a thermal sensor is its *thermal capacity*. The bigger this is, the longer the response time. Bead thermistors have the lowest thermal capacity. A low thermal capacity also means that, when a thermistor is placed in a small quantity of liquid, for example, to measure its temperature, the previous

58

temperature of the thermistor does not greatly alter the temperature of the liquid.

Positive tempco thermistors are of two main types. The *over-temperature* type has a fairly constant and low (about 100Ω) resistance at temperatures below a given set point (for example 80° or 120°C). As temperature increases above that point, resistance rises rapidly to about 10kΩ. In the *over-current* type resistance increases rapidly with temperature. The thermistor is wired in series with a load. The resistance of the thermistor is low at normal currents but excessive current causes the resistance to increase. The additional resistance protects the load by reducing the flow of current through it. Over-current thermistors are specified for maximum currents in the range 15mA to 350mA. 15mA types have a resistance of 1kΩ, while 350mA types have a resistance of 10Ω, until the current exceeds the specified maximum.

(ii) Bandgap sensors: These have the advantage of a linear output and low thermal capacity (see previous paragraph). The LM35CZ temperature sensor, connected as in Figure 16, gives an output in the range 0V to 1.1V over the range 0°C

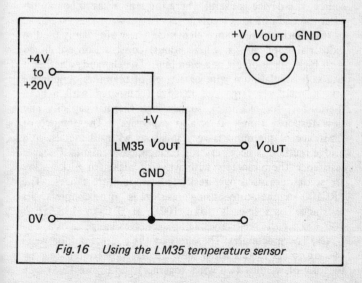

Fig.16   Using the LM35 temperature sensor

to 110°C, a voltage change of 10mV per degree Celsius. It can also be connected so as to operate over the range −40°C to 110°C, with an output of −0.04V to +1.1V. It has an accuracy of ±0.4°C at 25°C and ±0.8°C over its whole range. The LM35DZ is a cheaper version with an accuracy of ±0.6°C at 25°C, and an operating range of 0°C to 100°C. These two devices have the advantage that the voltage output is directly proportional to the *Celsius* temperature. This means that a temperature rise from, say, 10°C to 20°C doubles the output voltage. The LM335Z is even cheaper than the LM34DZ, is almost as precise, but its output is proportional to the *kelvin* temperature. A rise of temperature from 10°C (283K) to 20°C (293K) increases the output by only 3.5%. The LM3911 has an output directly proportional to the Celsius temperature. This ic includes a comparator so that the sensor's output voltage can be matched against a pre-set voltage, giving a logic-compatible output.

A device with a related function is the 590kH, a temperature-dependent *current* source (Fig.17). It regulates the current to $1\mu A$ per kelvin. Thus at 0°C (= 273K) the current is $273\mu A$. Its calibration accuracy is ±2.5K. Being a current source, the device is useful where the sensor has to be mounted at the end of a long lead.

(iii) Platinum resistance elements: These are mainly used in industrial applications, where robust construction combined with high precision are at a premium. The element, whether it is a coil of platinum wire or a track of platinum conductive ink, is relatively large and massive (compared with a bead thermistor, for example), so has high thermal capacity and slow response time. It is also expensive. The tempco of resistance of platinum is very small, as with all metals, so a bridge method is necessary for taking measurements. Cheaper resistance thermometers with wires of nickel or nickel-alloy are sometimes used over restricted temperature ranges. The PRC100 temperature-sensing resistor is an example. Its resistance rises linearly from 100Ω at 0°C to 138.5Ω at 100°C; note the relatively small percentage change.

(iv) Thermocouples: These rely on the contact p.d. between two dissimilar metals when they are placed in contact (e.g. by twisting or welding two wires together). In Figure 18(a) each

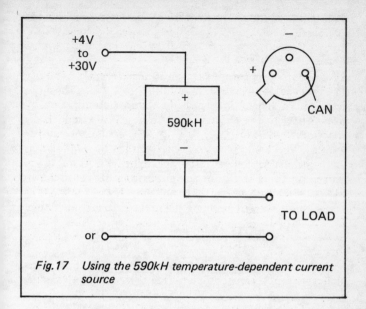

Fig.17   Using the 590kH temperature-dependent current source

junction produces a p.d. (E_1, E_2). If they are at equal temperatures $E_1 = E_2$ and they cancel out. If one junction is hotter than the other, as shown, $E_1 > E_2$ and a p.d. ($E_1 - E_2$) appears across the terminals. The commonly used iron/constantan (copper-nickel alloy) thermocouple gives an output of 5.4mV when the cold junction is at $0°C$ and the hot junction is at $100°C$. Output is reasonably linear over a wide range, allowing precise temperature measurements. An advantage of thermocouples is that the junction can be very small, especially if it is a butt joint, with a response time of a few milliseconds. In practice, only a single junction is necessary (Fig.18(b)) provided that the contacts between the probe and the measuring circuit are both at the same temperature. The actions of the copper-iron and constantan-copper junctions partly cancel out, giving the same effect as a single iron-constantan cold junction.

Thermocouples are typed according to the alloys used. Type K is the most commonly used, though type N has superior performance.

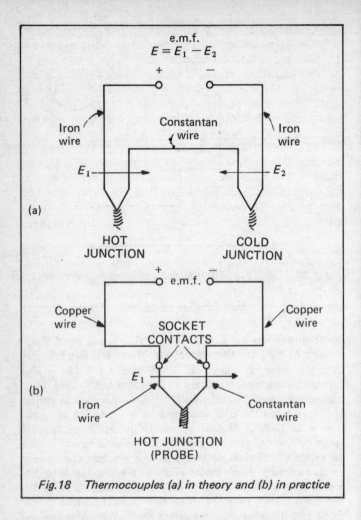

e.m.f.
$$E = E_1 - E_2$$

$+$ $-$

Iron wire

Constantan wire

Iron wire

E_1 →   ← E_2

(a)

HOT JUNCTION   COLD JUNCTION

$+$ $-$
e.m.f.

Copper wire

SOCKET CONTACTS

Copper wire

E_1 →

(b)

Iron wire   Constantan wire

HOT JUNCTION (PROBE)

Fig. 18   Thermocouples (a) in theory and (b) in practice

(v) **Temperature switches:** These consist of bimetallic switches which open or close at a given temperature. They are available for a range of temperatures, either as normally-closed switches which open at the fixed temperature, or normally open switches which close at that temperature. Once they have opened or closed, the reverse action occurs at a temperature about 15°C lower. Such switches are suitable for a wide range of applications, including switching mains-powered lamps, fans or small motors.

(vi) Pyroelectric devices: These are sensitive to the *rate of change* in the intensity of thermal (IR) radiation reaching them rather than to the absolute level of radiation. Their peak response is when the rate of change is in the region of 0.3–0.5 Hz. Their response time is less than 25 ms. When used in passive IR intruder detectors, the sensor is located behind a special plastic 'lens' which divides the area in front into fields. The fields are so arranged that a person *moving* through the area frequently passes from one field to another. This causes rapid *changes* in the intensity of IR reaching the sensor.

Strain gauges

The metal-foil strain gauge consists of a thin metal foil supported on an insulating backing. The gauge is cemented to the object that is to be put under stress, so that the axis along which the conductors lie is parallel with the direction of greatest strain. Gauges are also manufactured from semi-conducting materials.

The output of a strain gauge depends on its *gauge factor:*

$$\frac{\text{change in resistance}}{\text{resistance}} \times \frac{\text{length}}{\text{change in length}}$$

Gauges factors of 2 to 5 are typical of metal foil strain gauges, while those of semiconductor gauges are in the region 50–200. Given that the maximum strain that the gauge can be subjected to must not be more than a 3% to 4% extension of its length, the proportionate change in resistance of a strain gauge under normal working conditions is small. Usually it is measured by using a bridge method.

The tempco of most gauges is small but a more serious temperature error may arise when the object under stress is metal. Thermal expansion of the object forces the gauge to expand or contract too, altering its resistance. Strain gauges are available which are compensated for attachment to particular metals, including stainless steel, mild steel and aluminium.

Pressure sensors

Piezo-resistive pressure sensors are available as integrated circuits, used for measuring pressure in gases and liquids. The ic includes one or more sensors and resistors connected to form a bridge. The output of the bridge is almost linearly related to pressure. A typical sensor gives 0.6mV for each kilopascal of pressure, over the range 0 to 100kPa (100kPa is approximately one atmosphere). The less expensive ic's have a high tempco. Typically, the output falls by about 0.2% for each degree Celsius rise in temperature. Some ic's have a built-in thermistor to provide temperature compensation.

Microphones

The sensitivity of a microphone is quoted in decibels as 20 $\log_{10}(V/p)$, where V is the root mean square output in volts and p is the effective pressure of the sound. This is usually measured at a standard frequency of 1kHz. The effective pressure for quoting microphone sensitivity is usually taken as 1μbar, thus $p = 1$. If the r.m.s. output at that pressure is 1V, the sensitivity of the microphone is 20 $\log_{10}(1/1)$ = 0dB. Microphones produce less than 1V/μbar so their sensitivity ratings are negative when expressed in decibels. Often the peak voltage V_{PEAK} is measured, where V in the above expression is 0.707 $\times$ V_{PEAK}. The expression then becomes:

$$\text{sensitivity} = 20 \log_{10}(V_{PEAK} \times 0.707)$$

Thus a microphone giving peak output of 500μV/μbar has a sensitivity of 20 $\log_{10}(500 \times 10^{-6} \times 0.707)$ = −69dB. The lower the sensitivity, the more negative the figure in decibels. Sensitivity in decibels may be converted to r.m.s. output by using the inverse formula:

$$V = \frac{10^{\text{sensitivity}/20}}{0.707}$$

For example, if the sensitivity is quoted as −60dB, the r.m.s. output for p = 1 is:

$$V = \frac{10^{-60/20}}{0.707} = \frac{10^{-3}}{0.707} = 1414\mu V$$

The main types of microphone in common use are:

(i) **Moving coil (dynamic):** Compact; good linearity; low output impedance (about 150Ω) often switchable to high impedance (about 50kΩ). Sensitivity ranges from about −60dB to −80dB. Response range from about 80Hz to 13kHz, though highest-quality microphones of this type have a range from 50Hz to 15kHz.

(ii) **Quartz crystal piezo-electric:** Response inferior to that of dynamic microphone; high output impedance (about 1MΩ); small output e.m.f. May need an FET pre-amplifier in the microphone case if the microphone is on a long cable. Microphone and cable must be shielded; amplifier requires battery or external power supply. A specialised type is the ultrasonic microphone (or transducer) which has the crystal cut so as to resonate at a particular frequency, such as 40kHz.

(iii) **Electret:** A version of the capacitor microphone; the dielectric has a permanent electric field so this type generates an e.m.f. Excellent frequency response from 50Hz to 16kHz, the best of the types listed here; moderately high output impedance (typically 600Ω); rather low sensitivity level, around −64dB. Amplifier may be required.

Hall effect sensors
Different devices have different types of output. Some have digital (binary) output, affected either by the direction or the strength of the field and thus may be latching or non-latching. Others have an output which is linearly proportional to field strength − see table on page 66.

Hall effect sensors usually have an open-collector output requiring a pull-up resistor wired to the positive supply. A positive field is produced by the north-seeking pole of a permanent magnet directed at the designated 'sensitive side' of the device. The device can also be operated by a solenoid.

Type	Action	Field strength to turn on (output high)	to turn off (output low)
HS16	Binary, latching, field direction (surface mount device)	>+10mT	<—10mT
TL170C	Binary, latching, field direction	>+25mT	<—25mT
TL172C	Binary, non-latching, field strength	>+45mT	<+22mT
UGN3020U	Binary, non-latching, field strength	>+22mT	<+16.5mT
		Range	
634SS2	2 linear outputs	−40mT to +40mT	
HS94A	Linear output (surface mount device)	−50mT to +50mT	

Reed switches

A reed switch consists of two springy metal contacts sealed in a capsule. In a magnetic field, the contacts become temporarily magnetised, attract each other, and close together. Reed switches are less sensitive than Hall effect devices but they require no external components. They are used as position sensors, for example to detect open doors and windows in security systems. Reed switches are used in reed relays in which the magnetic field is provided by the energising coil. Their advantage is that their closing time is only 1 or 2 milliseconds, about one-tenth the operating time of electromagnetic relays.

Gas sensors

A gas sensor contains two elements, the sensor and the compensator, enclosed beneath a dome of stainless steel mesh. The mesh is to prevent explosions possibly being caused by the spread of combustion within the dome spreading to an inflammable atmosphere outside. In the presence of certain combustible gases the resistance of the sensor element increases relatively to that of the compensator element. The disparity in their resistance is measured by connecting the sensor and compensator in a half-bridge. Gases that are detectable by sensors such as this include isobutane, methane (present in natural gas and town gas), hydrogen and ethanol (alcohol). Most gas sensors require a supply of at least 150 mA, which makes it difficult to use them in a battery-powered unit. The voltage across the bridge (and hence across the elements) must be carefully regulated, usually to 2.2V or 3V depending on the type of sensor. Care must be taken not to over-run the elements as they burn out easily.

15 Meters

Meters are subdivided into two main types, analogue (with scale and needle) and digital (numeric display). The analogue type are further subdivided into moving-coil and moving-iron meters. Moving-iron meters have the advantage that they are able to measure alternating voltages and currents. Their main disadvantage is that their scale is non-linear and is usually not easy or even possible to take accurate measurements near the zero end of the scale. Such meters are usually rated for currents of several amps and for the higher voltage ranges (up to 500V).

Selecting a meter

The choice of meter usually rests between a moving-coil meter and a digital meter — see table on page 68.

Measuring d.c. voltage

A moving-coil meter used for measuring voltage consists of the meter movement (which is essentially a milliammeter or microammeter) and a *series resistor* of suitable value. Ready-made voltmeters have the series resistor incorporated but a microammeter or milliammeter may readily be used as a voltmeter by wiring a suitable resistor in series with the coil (Fig.19). Choose a meter with a coil resistance of 1kΩ or preferably more. If the meter has a full-scale deflection (fsd) of I (in amps) with coil resistance $r\Omega$, and the required fsd deflection is V (in volts), then the required series resistance (in ohms) given by:

$$R = (V/I) - r$$

Feature	Moving-coil	Digital
Accuracy	1.5% to 2.5%	0.1% (±1 count) or better
Input impedance	Low; <1Ω for ammeters; few kΩ for voltmeters	High, usually 10MΩ
Operating power	None required	Typically 100mA or more for LED display; 150μA for an LCD display
Readability	Easy to follow fast changes	Confusing to follow changing digits
	Easy to reach end-points	Time-consuming, as display is being updated every 3s (typically)
	Parallax problems	Precise to 3½ or 4½ figures*
Polarity	Usually unipolar, but centre-zero types are available	Often have automatic polarity
Physical size	Necessarily large	Can be very small
Mechanical	Easily damaged by shock	More robust
Cost	Less than £10	More than £20

* assuming that the test circuit is capable of producing a correspondingly precise output; if not, the final digit (or two digits) may be misleadingly meaningless.

For example, if a 100μA meter, coil resistance 3750Ω, is to be used at fsd of 5V:

$$R = \frac{5}{100 \times 10^{-6}} - 3750 = 46250\Omega$$

A 47kΩ resistor, 2% tolerance would normally be suitable.

Whereas moving-coil meters essentially measure current, digital meters usually measure voltage. Typically their fsd is 200mV. Larger voltages are measured by using two resistors

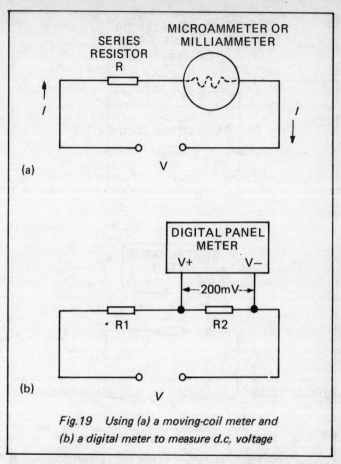

*Fig.19   Using (a) a moving-coil meter and
(b) a digital meter to measure d.c. voltage*

as a potential divider (see Fig.19 and p.77). For example, to convert the fsd from 200mV to 20V, R1 = 1MΩ and R2 = 10kΩ.

Measuring direct current

A moving-coil meter used for measuring current consists of the meter movement and a *shunt resistor* of suitable value. Ready-made ammeters have the shunt resistor incorporated but a milliammeter may be used to measure greater currents

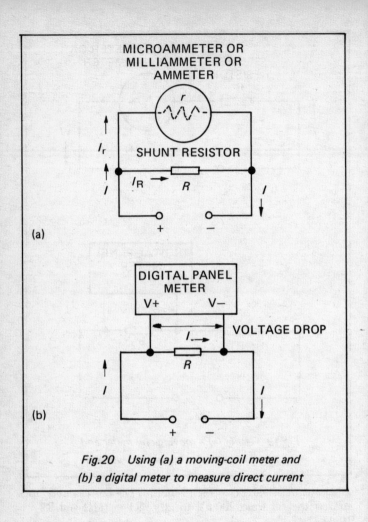

MICROAMMETER OR
MILLIAMMETER OR
AMMETER

r

SHUNT RESISTOR

I_r

I

I_R $\quad$ R

I

+ $\qquad$ −

(a)

DIGITAL PANEL
METER

V+ $\qquad$ V−

VOLTAGE DROP

$I_{\rightarrow}$

R

I $\qquad\qquad$ I

+ $\qquad$ −

(b)

*Fig.20 Using (a) a moving-coil meter and
(b) a digital meter to measure direct current*

by wiring a suitable resistor in parallel with the coil (Fig.20). Choose a meter with a coil resistance less than 100Ω. If the meter has a full-scale deflection (fsd) of I (in amps) with coil resistance $r\Omega$, the required fsd is I_{REQ}, then the required shunt resistance (in ohms) is given by:

70

$$R = \frac{rI}{I_{REQ} - I}$$

For example, if a 100mA meter, coil resistance 50Ω, is to be used at fsd of 5A:

$$R = \frac{50 \times 100 \times 10^{-3}}{5 - 100 \times 10^{-3}} = 1.02\Omega$$

The minimum power rating of the resistor (p.13) is $P = I^2 R = 25.5$W. A higher power rating is preferred so that heating will not affect the value of the resistor. Such a resistor may be difficult to obtain ready-made, although it is possible to wind one, using constantan wire. Certain types of meter are available for which shunts can be purchased to convert them to a number of different fsd's.

For measuring current with a digital meter we usually measure the voltage drop across a known resistor (Fig.20). For example, given a fsd of 200mV, and a requirement to measure 50mA fsd, the resistor is $(200 \times 10^{-3})/(50 \times 10^{-3})$ = 4Ω. The minimum power rating of the resistor is $I^2R = (50 \times 10^{-3})^2 \times 4 = 10$mW. Probably the easiest way to obtain this is to use three 12Ω resistors in parallel.

Errors of measurement
Current: the parallel resistance of the meter and shunts, if any, is in series with the test circuit and reduces the current flowing. As the resistances are usually much less than the circuit resistances, the error is very small.

Voltage: serious error can arise when a low-impedance meter (i.e. moving coil meter) is used to measure the voltage in a high-impedance circuit. A typical example is the potential divider in Figure 21. Voltmeters are rated in ohms per volt. This is the total resistance of the meter coil and series resistor divided by the fsd voltage. Thus a meter rated at 2kΩ/V and 10V fsd has a resistance of 20kΩ. In the figure the theoretical voltage at point A is $(10 \times 22)/(22 + 47) = 3.2$V. With the meter connected as shown, the resistance of the meter is in parallel with that of R2, reducing the resistance of the bottom

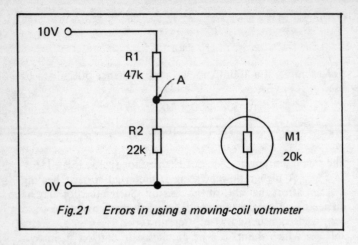

Fig.21 Errors in using a moving-coil voltmeter

half of the potential divider to $10.5\text{k}\Omega$. This reduces the potential at point A to $(10 \times 10.5)/(10.5 + 47) = 1.8\text{V}$, a very serious error. There are 3 solutions to this problem:

(i)   use a moving-coil meter with a higher resistance coil; this will be considerably more expensive;

(ii) use a digital meter with high input impedance; this will have virtually no effect on the potential at A, but is more expensive;

(iii) connect point A to an operational amplifier wired as a voltage follower (p.108) and measure its output using the low-resistance voltmeter.

16 Heat sinks
The aim of heat sinking is to prevent the collector-emitter junction of a transistor (or its equivalent in other semiconductor devices) from exceeding its safe maximum temperature, T_j. For silicon transistors T_j is about $150°\text{C}$, though certain types are rated to operate up to $180°\text{C}$. For germanium devices it is only $85°\text{C}$.

The thermal resistance of an object or layer is denoted by:

$$\theta = (T_1 - T_2)/P_o$$

expressed in $°C/W$ where, when power P_o is being dissipated, heat is passing from a hotter region at T_1 to a cooler region at T_2. The total thermal resistance θ_T between the junction at T_j and the surrounding air, at ambient temperature T_a of a transistor mounted on a heat sink is the sum of 3 such thermal resistances:

θ_i, *intrinsic* thermal resistance between the junction and the transistor case: if values are not given in the manufacturer's data sheet, they may be calculated from other data. For example, the TIP3055 is quoted to have a maximum power dissipation (P_o) of 90W at case temperature T_c of $25°C$. Assuming maximum junction temperature of $150°C$, then $\theta_i = (150 - 25)/90 = 1.4°C/W$.

θ_w, thermal resistance of the insulating *washer*, from one surface to the other. See data sheets; values typically range between 0.05 and $0.65°C/W$. If no washer is used, a value of approximately $1.3°C/W$ should be allowed for dry thermal contact between the transistor and the heat sink, or $0.7°C/W$ if silicone grease is used. Silicone rubber washers need no grease. With washers of other types, greasing reduces thermal resistance to about 30–50%.

θ_s, thermal resistance of the *sink*, from the surface of attachment of the transistor to surfaces in contact with air. See data sheets; values range from $85°C/W$ for a small push-on TO5 heat sink to $0.23°C/W$ for a large and multifinned heat sink. Sinks with a black anodised finish have lower thermal resistance than those with a bright metallic surface. Values are quoted for the heat sink being mounted with fins vertical to allow convection to occur. Mounting with fins horizontal reduces efficiency by up to 70%.

Ambient temperature is often taken as $25°C$; this value may be used if the heat sink is exposed, for instance it is mounted on the outside of the instrument case. If the sink is enclosed in the case, ambient may be much higher, depending on the total power being dissipated by the circuit, and by the extent of ventilation. A figure of $70°C$ can be taken as a likely value, though actual measurements should be made if in doubt.

Calculating maximum allowable power dissipation: Find the total thermal resistance, allowing for grease, if any, by reducing θ_w' proportionately:

$$\theta_T = \theta_i + \theta_w + \theta_s$$

Then calculate (assuming maximum junction temperature of 150°C):

$$P_o = \frac{150 - T_A}{\theta_T}$$

Example: A transistor with $\theta_i = 1.5°C/W$ is mounted on a heat sink with $\theta_s = 2.1°C/W$, using a conductive washer (no grease required) with $\theta_w = 0.05°C/W$. Ambient temperature within the equipment case is 70°C. Calculate P the maximum allowable power dissipation in the transistor.

$$\theta_T = 1.5 + 0.05 + 2.1 = 3.65°C/W$$

$$P = (150 - 70)/3.65 = 22W$$

Calculating the thermal resistance of the heat sink required:

$$\theta_s = \frac{150 - T_A}{P_o} - \theta_i - \theta_w$$

Example: In the example above, suppose that the transistor is required to operate at 10W. Calculate θ_s.

$$\theta = \left((150 - 70)/10\right) - 1.5 - 0.05 = 6.45°C/W$$

Select a heat sink with a slightly lower rating, e.g. 4°C/W.

17 Wire

For most constructional purposes, especially for the hobbyist, only four types of wire are required:

Solid core wire

Also known as bell wire; single core of 0.6mm diameter copper wire (1/0.6); current rating 1.8A at 70°C; voltage rating

1000V rms; insulation 0.3mm sheath of PVC available in a wide range of colours; overall diameter 1.2mm. Ideal for wiring pcbs, stripboard, panels and chassis.

Stranded wire
Also known as hook-up wire; there are various types but a useful wire has 7 strands 0.2mm in diameter (7/0.2); current rating 1.4A at 70°C; voltage rating 1000V rms; insulation 0.3mm sheath of PVC, available in a wide range of colours; overall diameter 1.2mm. Unsuitable for wiring up pcb's and stripboard as it is difficult to ensure that all the strands are pushed through the holes, risking short-circuits through stray strands. Ideal for inter-board connections, panel wiring, inter-equipment connections.

Light duty stranded wire
Has 10 strands 0.1mm in diameter (10/0.1); current rating 0.5A at 70°C; voltage rating 750V rms; insulation 0.25mm sheath of PVC, available in several colours; overall diameter 1.05mm. Useful where extra flexibility is required (e.g. connections to probes) or where many wires have to be packed into a small space.

Mains cable
A range of 2-core and 3-core flexible cables is available rated for various maximum currents. 3-core 3A cable is probably the most useful for small equipment that requires the case to be earthed.

Chapter 3

ANALOGUE CIRCUITS

1 Potential dividers

This is a simple way to produce a smaller voltage from a larger one. Figure 22 shows the basic divider in which:

$$V_{OUT} = V_{IN} \times \frac{R2}{R1 + R2}$$

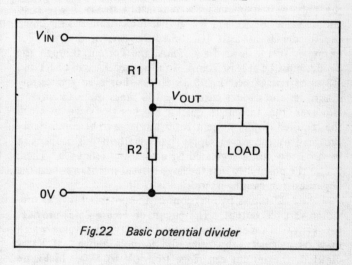

Fig.22   Basic potential divider

The stability of V_{OUT} depends essentially on the stability of V_{IN}. It also depends upon the current being drawn from the divider. In effect, R2 is in parallel with the load so that, if the load has low resistance, the total resistance of the lower part of the divider is seriously reduced. This leads to a fall of V_{OUT}. An example is given on p.72, where the load is a voltmeter with a low-resistance coil.

Assuming that the load draws negligible current, the precision of V_{OUT} depends on the precision of both V_{IN} and the resistors. Given a precise value for V_{IN} and resistors of identical tolerance, the tolerance range of V_{OUT} is the same as the tolerance of the resistors. If the resistors have equal tempcos, V_{OUT} has zero tempco. To ensure that both resistors are subjected to a similar temperature regime and have very similar tempco, use resistors in a resistor network package. Using these, and possibly connecting several of the resistors in series, one can build dividers in which R1 = R2, R1 = 2 × R2, 3 × R1 = 4 × R2, etc., to obtain a range of output values.

If the load draws a reasonably constant current, it is possible to compensate for the resulting fall in V_{OUT} by increasing the value of R2. If the load draws variable current, the only way to maintain a reasonably steady V_{OUT} is to choose values of R1 and R2 so that the current passing down the divider is at least ten times the current drawn. For example, if the load draws 5mA, the current through the divider must be at least 50mA. In this case, the sum of R1 and R2 must not exceed $V_{IN}/0.05$ ohms. For even greater precision, let the divider current be 100 times the load current. However, this technique quickly reaches the stage at which the required divider current is far too large to be comfortably provided by the power supply, particularly if this happens to be a battery, or is regulated by a band-gap reference. There is also the possibility that the large current might over-heat the larger resistor, causing its resistance to alter.

Figure 23 shows two versions of the potential divider providing variable output. The circuit of Figure 23(a) provides for V_{OUT} to range continuously from 0V to a value which may be calculated by using the formula above. If R1 is omitted, the output can range from 0V to V_{IN}. In Figure 23(b), V_{OUT} is adjustable over a narrow range not including the extremes, with a greater precision than is obtainable in Figure 23(a).

2 Voltage stabilisers

The most precise way to stabilise a voltage is to use a band-gap voltage reference (p.42), but the amount of current available from such a circuit is often limited to a few (typically 5) milliamps. A few references allow a higher current, but the upper limit is about 150mA. If a reasonably well stabilised

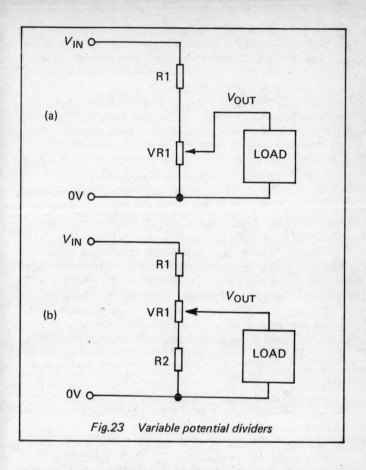

Fig.23   Variable potential dividers

voltage is required at currents in excess of 100mA, a 3-terminal voltage regulator may be used. Regulators of this kind are described on pages 307 to 317.

In this section we explore the use of the Zener diode as a voltage stabiliser. Figure 24 shows the basic circuit. As explained on page 32 Zeners are available with a wide range of Zener voltages but, before selecting the device to use, it is essential to know what current is to be supplied to the load. The Zener voltage quoted in the data sheet applies only to

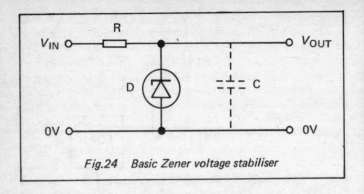

Fig.24   Basic Zener voltage stabiliser

one particular Zener current, which may or may not be quoted. As an estimate, take this to be 5mA. This is the minimum current passing through the Zener when the load is taking its maximum current. The maximum current the Zener will be required to pass, when the load is taking no current, is the load current plus 5mA. Given the maximum current I_{MAX}, and the Zener voltage, V_Z, the power dissipated in the Zener is $P = I_{MAX}.V_Z$. This gives the minimum power rating required. Next calculate the value of the dropping resistor R. This has to drop the voltage from V_{IN} to V_Z (or just above), with a current I_{MAX} passing through it. Thus, $R = (V_{IN} - V_Z)/I_{MAX}$.

Example: The power supply voltage is 9V and it is required to produce a stabilised 4.7V, for a load that takes up to 250 mA. First calculate I_{MAX} = 250 + 5 = 255mA. The power dissipation is 255mA × 4.7V = 1.2W. The BZX85 series (1.3W) would be just possible, although it would be safer to use a diode from the 1N5333 series (5W, see p.33). To drop the voltage by 4.3V at 255mA requires R = 4.3/0.255 = 16.9Ω. Use a lower value, such as 15Ω. The power rating for this resistor should be at least $(0.255)^2$ × 15 = 0.98W. A 1W resistor could be used but a 2W resistor is preferred.

A further addition to the circuit may be required in certain circumstances. A reverse-biased Zener is a source of voltage noise, which will be added to the output voltage. In most applications this will not be a problem but, if it is required to eliminate it, connect a capacitor (10n to 100n) where shown in the figure.

The cut-off voltage is not perfectly constant and tends to rise with increasing Zener current. This means that the voltage rises slightly when the load takes less current. The change of voltage with change of current is known as the *slope resistance*. A slope resistance of 2Ω, for example means that an increase of current of 1mA produces a change in voltage of 2mV. Thus a change of 250mA in the example above will lead to a change in voltage of 0.5V. As the 4.7V Zener in the 1N5333 series is so rated at a test current of 260mA, and has a maximum slope resistance of 2Ω, the output of the circuit is 4.7V at low load current 250mA, falling to 4.2V when the load is maximal. This is the worst case condition. In general slope resistances are higher than this, particularly for Zeners rated for lower voltages and for those rated at over 50V. This sets a limit on the usefulness of a single Zener as a stabilizer.

Figure 25 shows two variations on the basic circuit. Two Zeners may be wired in series to obtain a voltage that is the sum of their individual voltages. In Figure 25(b) the first Zener D1 reduces the voltage part of the way (V_{INT}) toward the required level. More important, it shunts away the excess current when the demand by the load is low. This means that D2 does not have to cope with such a wide range of currents and hence the effect of slope resistance is reduced. A much more stable voltage is obtained.

A programmable form of Zener diode is seen in Figure 26. R1 is the voltage dropping resistor, as before, but we now have two programming resistors VR1 and R2, acting as a potential divider to produce a reference voltage. The relationship is:

$$V_{OUT} = 2.75(1 + VR1/R2)$$

This device gives good stabilisation at any voltage between V_{REF} (which should be about 2.5V) and 36V. The Zener current, and hence the load current, is between 1mA and 100mA.

If higher currents are required the circuit of Figure 27 overcomes the difficulties associated with slope resistance. The transistor (which can be a high-current power transistor) is biased into conduction by I_B passing through the resistor.

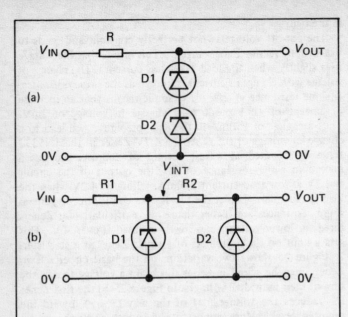

Fig.25 Zener diode stabilisers: (a) to obtain non-standard voltage; (b) to obtain improved stabilisation

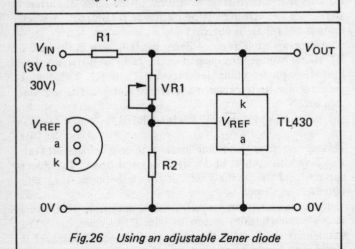

Fig.26 Using an adjustable Zener diode

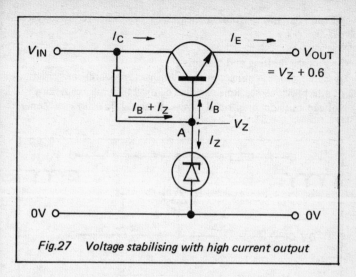

Fig.27   Voltage stabilising with high current output

The voltage at point A is held constant by the Zener. If the load takes more current, the emitter voltage begins to fall, increasing the base-emitter voltage and turning the transistor further on. More current flows. The converse happens if the load takes less current. The current to the Zener varies very little and so slope resistance has little effect. The output voltage of this circuit equals the Zener voltage plus the base-emitter .drop of 0.6V. For example, V_{OUT} is 5.3V with a 4.7V Zener. Since the current to the Zener is relatively small, only a low-wattage Zener is required.

The value of the resistor is calculated as follows. Assume V_{IN} = 9V. If the maximum current required is 2A, and the gain of the transistor is 20 (the minimum for a BD131), the maximum I_B is 100mA. I_Z is 5mA, so that R has to pass 105mA and drop 4.3V, the value of R is 4.3/0.105 = 41Ω. A 39Ω resistor is suitable. The power rating of this is 39 × 0.105^2 = 0.43W. A 0.5W resistor is within range. The maximum power dissipated in the Zener is 4.7 × 0.105 = 0.5W. A BZX79 series Zener (0.5W) could be used, although a BZX61 Zener (1.3W) would be safer. The transistor drops the voltage by 3.7V. The maximum power is 2 × 3.7 = 7.4W. A BD131 transistor is rated for 15W so this is well within its rating, but a heat sink may be required (see p.72).

3 Voltage limiting and clamping
A Zener diode, connected as in the voltage stabilising circuits of the previous section, can also be used to limit excursions of voltage outside prescribed limits. Figure 28(a) shows a Zener

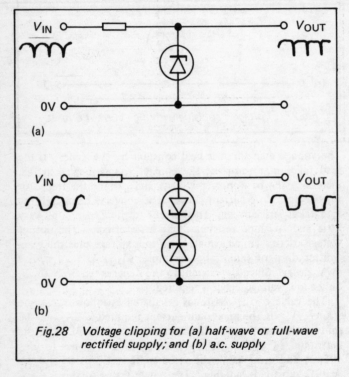

Fig.28   Voltage clipping for (a) half-wave or full-wave rectified supply; and (b) a.c. supply

diode being used to clip the waveform of a full-wave power supply. Instead of a power supply voltage this could be an input signal, such as the input to a metering circuit, which must not be allowed to exceed a given voltage. The calculations involved are the same as those given above, basing them on the peak voltage of V_{IN}. In Figure 28(b), two Zeners are wired back-to-back to limit an a.c. signal or power supply in a similar way. The only possible limitation of this type of circuit is if the capacitance of the Zener makes the circuit act as a low-pass filter (p.121). The effect of this can be calculated using the normal filter equations, but is unlikely to have any serious effect until the frequency exceeds 300kHz. Figure 29

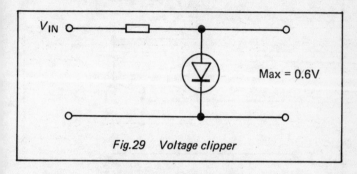

Fig.29   Voltage clipper

shows an ordinary silicon diode being used to limit V_{OUT} to 0.6V, the forward voltage drop of the diode.

One important aspect of voltage limiting is concerned with the excessively high voltages that are sometimes generated by inductive components. The classic example is the relay coil switched by a transistor (Fig.30). When the transistor is switched off the rapid collapse of the magnetic field in the relay coil causes a high transient voltage to appear at the collector of the transistor. This can be several hundred volts and will eventually lead to breakdown of the transistor. The diode connected as in Figure 30 clamps the collector voltage to that of the supply and this protects the transistor. Normally a 1N4148 diode may be used.

The circuits of Figure 31 show how a diode is used to clamp a voltage to vary within a range different from the range of V_{IN}. In each case the capacitor prevents the d.c. level of V_{IN} being carried across to V_{OUT}; it is only voltage *swings* (e.g. alternating signals or pulses) that are transferred through the capacitor. At (a) the input signal ranges between 0V and a positive voltage which, for the sake of the description, we take to be +6V. On the other side of the capacitor,

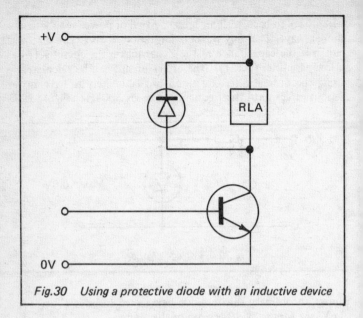

Fig.30 Using a protective diode with an inductive device

in the absence of the diode, the signal would range from $-3V$ to $+3V$, so reaching only half the peak positive level. The diode discharges the capacitor when V_{IN} falls to zero, so V_{OUT} falls to zero too. As V_{IN} rises toward $+6V$, V_{OUT} rises to $+6V$. This account does not allow for the forward voltage drop of the diode. In practice V_{OUT} is 0.6V lower than V_{IN}, and ranges from $-0.6V$ to $+5.4V$. Thus the signal levels are restored to almost their original levels.

The circuit of Figure 31(b) has a similar action, the output being clamped to 0V. As V_{IN} ranges from 0V to $+6V$, V_{OUT} ranges from $-5.4V$ to $+0.6V$. In Figure 31(c), with the same input, the output is clamped to $+10V$ and ranges from $+10.6V$ to $+16.6V$.

4 Voltage converters

The circuits described here are based on the 7660 voltage conversion ic. Figure 32 illustrates the way in which the ic is used as a voltage inverter. V_{OUT} has the same value as the supply, but with the opposite polarity. This is a handy way of

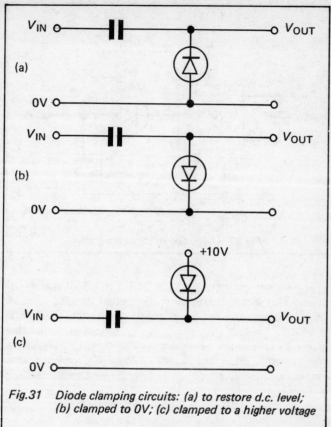

Fig.31   Diode clamping circuits: (a) to restore d.c. level;
(b) clamped to 0V; (c) clamped to a higher voltage

producing a negative voltage (for powering a few op amps,
for example) without having to instal a dual-rail supply. The
connection between pin 6 and the 0V rail is used only when
the supply voltage is 3.5V or less. The diode is required only
when the supply voltage is 6.5V or more. With the diode in
circuit the output voltage is reduced by the forward voltage
drop of the diode. In Figure 32 a germanium diode is used,
so the drop is only about 0.3V.

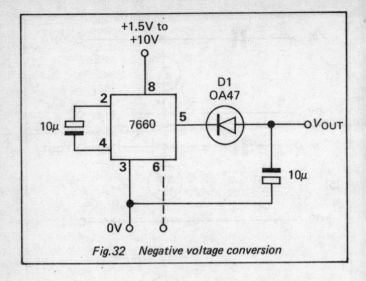

Fig.32   Negative voltage conversion

The output impedance of the device is approximately 70 ohms. This means that, unless the current demand is small (i.e. for powering CMOS op amps), the output voltage is numerically smaller than the input by an amount depending on the current drain. To calculate the output voltage for a given current, given the supply voltage V_S, and the load current I):

$$V_{OUT} = -V_S + (70 \times I)$$

Example: if $V_S = 9$ and I = 5mA, the $V_{OUT} = -9 + (70 \times 0.005) = -8.65V$. Since the supply voltage is over 6.5V, reduce the calculated V_{OUT} by 0.3V to allow for the diode, making $V_{OUT} = -8.35V$.

In Figure 33 the oscillator of the 7660 is used in conjunction with a diode pump to give a positive V_{OUT} which is double the supply, minus twice the forward voltage drop of the diodes. For example, if the supply is 6V and silicon diodes are used, with forward voltage drop 0.6V:

$$V_{OUT} = 2(6 - 0.6) = 10.8V$$

88

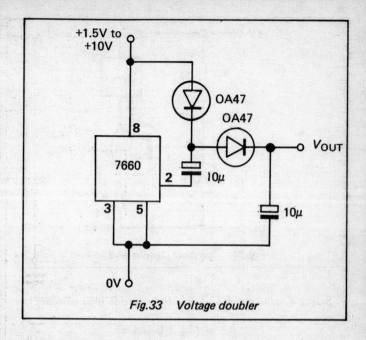

Fig.33   Voltage doubler

The output impedance in this circuit is about 60Ω.

5 Constant current circuits

The use of constant current 'diodes' (actually JFETs) is described on p.33, and the LM334Z constant current source is described on p.43. These two devices cover many requirements but three further methods of obtaining constant current are detailed below.

(i) **Constant current sink:** In Figure 34 a transistor has its biassing voltage held steady by a Zener diode. The design procedure is: Select a value for R1 to give a reasonable working current (about 5mA) through the Zener.

$$R1 = (V - V_Z)/0.005$$

Example: if $V = 9$ and $V_Z = 5.1$, then R1 = 780Ω. A resistor of 820Ω would be suitable.

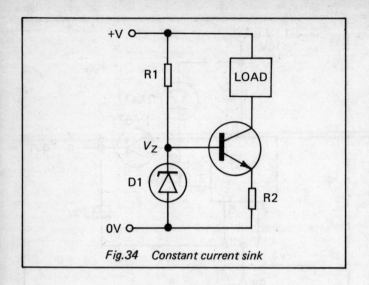

Fig.34   Constant current sink

Select a value for R2 to give the required load current, I:

$$R2 = (V_Z - 0.6)/I$$

Example: in the example above, if I = $450\mu A$, then R2 = $(5.1 - 0.6)/(450 \times 10^{-6})$ = 10kΩ.

The maximum allowable load resistance is given by:

$$R = (V - V_Z)/I$$

Any greater load resistance than this will cause the voltage drop across the load to exceed the drop across R1, which would reverse-bias the collector-base junction.

Example: the maximum load resistance is $(9 - 5.1)/450 \times 10^{-6})$ = 8.7kΩ.

In the example above a constant current of $450\mu A$ will flow for all load resistances up to 8.7kΩ. The current falls with higher resistances.

(ii) Temperature stable current sources: The LM334Z can be wired to give zero tempco by using the circuit of Figure 10(b), p.44. Another zero tempco current source is shown in

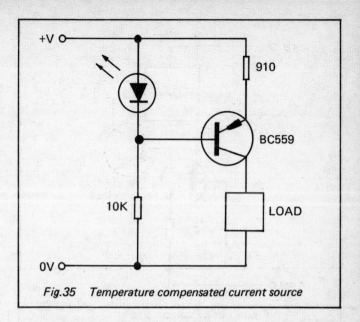

Fig.35   Temperature compensated current source

Figure 35. Here the tempco of the LED compensates for the equal tempco of the base-emitter junction of the silicon *pnp* transistor. The result is that the current of approximately 1mA varies by less than 1% over the temperature range -55°C to 100°C. The supply voltage may be varied over the range 5V to 25V.

(iii) JFET current sinks: The use of a constant current 'diode' has already been described (p.33). This is really a JFET with its source and gate terminal connected. The current provided by this is the saturated drain current, I_{DSS}, of the transistor. An ordinary JFET may also be used in this way, giving a constant I_{DSS}, depending on what value this has for the individual transistor. However the current can be reduced below I_{DSS} by including a resistor between source and drain, as in Figure 36. The value of resistor required is found by trial.

A variation on this circuit is shown in Figure 37. It is particularly useful for sinking very small currents with high precision. The op amp is one with low input offset current,

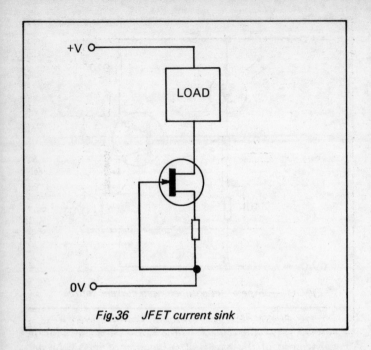

Fig.36   JFET current sink

low input offset voltage, and high input impedance. A bifet
op amp such as the TL081A is suitable. The sink current is
given by:

$$I = V_{IN}/R$$

V_{IN} should be about 1V and the value of R selected accordingly. Having selected R, adjust V_{IN} slightly to obtain the
required current. Figure 38 shows a version of this circuit
suitable for sinking currents up to 200mA. The transistor
must be rated to withstand the power dissipated within it if
the current is large.

6 Bipolar transistor amplifiers

(i) **Common emitter amplifiers**: This is probably the most
commonly used transistor amplifier (Fig.39), distinguished
from the other configurations by the fact that the emitter
connection is common to both the input and output sides of

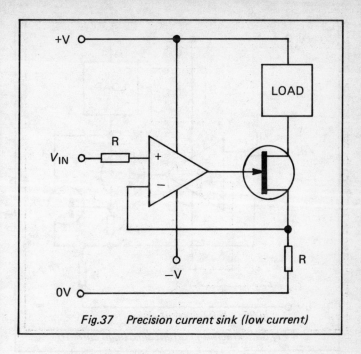

Fig.37   Precision current sink (low current)

the amplifier. The emitter resistor R_E is not an essential feature of this amplifier; the emitter of the transistor can be connected directly to the 0V rail. The function of R_E is to provide feedback, limiting the gain of the amplifier but improving its stability. Variations in the input voltage are coupled to the amplifier by C1. They appear as variations in voltage across R_C, and are coupled to the following circuit by C2. The voltage amplification depends on the gain of the transistor and also on the value of R_C.

Common emitter amplifiers have medium voltage gain, high current gain and hence high power gain. Their input and output impedance is moderate, depending on the values of the biassing and collector resistors. They produce a 180° phase shift; i.e. the output signal is the inverse of the input signal.

Design stages: Decide on a suitable quiescent collector current; 1–2mA is a good value for reasonably low noise.

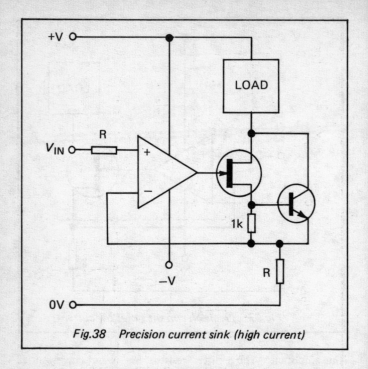

Fig.38 Precision current sink (high current)

Select R_C to make the collector voltage lie midway between the supply rail (at V_{CC}) and the ground rail (at 0V), i.e. $V_{CC}/2$. Choose R_B (Fig.39(a)) to give a suitable base current, assuming a typical average value for h_{fe}. Choose C1 and C2 so that they will pass all required frequencies.

Example: given that the supply voltage V_{CC} = 9V, and the transistor is a BC109 with typical gain 520 at 2mA. Minimum frequency to be passed is 30Hz. To obtain collector voltage of 4.5V, R_C = 4.5/0.002 = 2250Ω. Use standard 2.2kΩ resistor. A suitable value for R_E is 1kΩ. A current of 2mA through R_E brings the emitter voltage to 2V, making the base voltage 2 + 0.6 = 2.6V. The voltage drop across R_B is 9 − 2.6 = 6.4. The base current is 2mA/h_{fe} = 0.002/520 = 3.8μA. Therefore the value of R_B is 6.4/(3.8 × 10^{-6}) = 1.68MΩ. Use a standard 1.6MΩ resistor, or 1.5MΩ in series with 100kΩ. On the input side, R_B and C1 constitute a high-

94

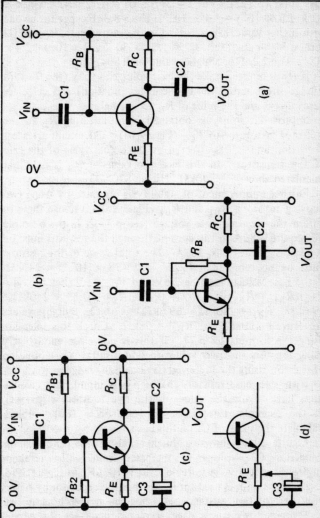

Fig.39 Common emitter amplifiers: (a) simple biassing;
(b) collector resistor biassing; (c) potential divider biassing;
(d) variable by-passing

pass filter (p.122). For f = 30Hz, $C1 = 1/(2\pi fR) = 1/(2\pi \times 30 \times 1.6 \times 10^6) = 3.3 \times 10^{-9}$. Use a 3.3nF capacitor or one with higher value, say 4.7nF. On the output side, R_C and C2 form a high-pass filter. $C2 = 1/2\pi \times 30 \times 2.2 \times 10^3) = 2.4 \times 10^{-6}$. Use 2.2$\mu$F or a higher value such as 4.7μF.

If R_E is omitted, take the base voltage as 0.6V (the forward voltage drop across the base-emitter junction) and calculate base current and the value of R_B accordingly.

Improved stability is obtained by connecting R_B to the collector instead of to V_{CC} (Fig.39(b)). The circuit gives less distortion and is less affected by the actual value of the gain of the transistor. In this case the value of R_B is half that calculated above, i.e. 840kΩ. Use an 820kΩ resistor.

Further improvement of stability is obtained by using two biassing resistors, R_{B1} and R_{B2} (Fig.39(c)). Choose these to obtain the required base voltage (see p.77). In the example we require 3.8μA so the current through the resistors must be at least 10 times this, 38μA. The total value of the resistors must be no more than $V_{CC}/I_B = 9/(38 \times 10^{-6}) = 240k\Omega$. If the base voltage is to be 2.6V and $V_{CC} = 9$V then the ratio $R_{B2}/(R_{B1} + R_{B2})$ is 2.6/9 = 0.29. $R_{B2} = 0.29 \times 240$k$\Omega = 69.6$kΩ. $R_{B1} = 240$k$\Omega - 69.6$k$\Omega = 170$kΩ. Suitable values are $R_{B1} = 160$kΩ and $R_{B2} = 68$kΩ. Check this selection using the formula on p.77. If this is not close enough, try using resistors of *lower* values to find a suitable combination of resistors using the preferred (E12 or E24) range.

With two base resistors the high-pass input filter calculations have to use the values of the two resistors in parallel. In the example, this is $(68 \times 160)/(68 + 160) = 48k\Omega$. Calculate the value of C1 on this basis.

Figure 39(c) shows a further refinement, the *by-pass* capacitor C3, leading to increased gain whilst retaining improved stability. A suitable value is 100μF. In Figure 39(d) a variable resistor is used for R_E so that the capacitor by-passes only part of the resistance, allowing the gain to be adjusted.

Temperature changes affect the forward voltage of the base-emitter junction and hence the performance of this amplifier. The addition of two forward-biased (i.e. with their cathodes toward the 0V rail) diodes in series with R_{B2} compensates for this, provided that $R_{B1} = R_{B2}$. This implies that the base

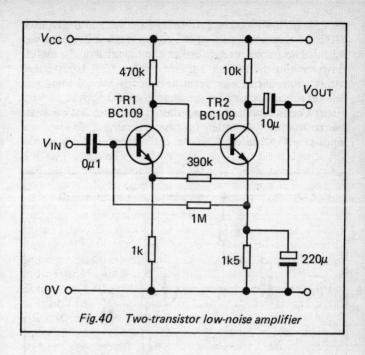

Fig.40   Two-transistor low-noise amplifier

voltage must be half of V_{CC}. To achieve this, select R_E so that, with the given quiescent current passing through it, the emitter voltage is $V_{CC}/2 - 0.6$. If this is not feasible, and R_{B1} is much larger than R_{B2}, then *approximate* temperature compensation is provided by just one diode in series with R_{B2}.

Figure 40 is a low-noise amplifier consisting of two cascaded common emitter amplifiers. They are direct-coupled together, this being possible because the collector voltage of TR1 is suitable as the base voltage of TR2. Both transistors are low-noise types, such as the BC109. To achieve lowest noise, the quiescent current through TR1 is very small (about 10–25μA). The quiescent current through TR2 is larger, about 700μA, giving approximately 1V across the emitter resistor of TR2. The biassing current for TR1 comes from the emitter of TR2, this giving rise to negative feedback from TR2 to TR1. This reduces the overall gain of the circuit but gives improved stability and freedom from distortion. Further

97

negative feedback occurs between the output and the emitter of TR1. The overall gain of the circuit is about 200, which is small. The output needs further amplification to be useful. However this circuit has amplified a low-level input signal without introducing significant noise; conventional amplifiers (see above) can be used for subsequent stages.

(ii) Common collector amplifier: This is also known as an *emitter-follower* amplifier because the output follows the input (Fig.41). In other words, the voltage gain is 1. It has

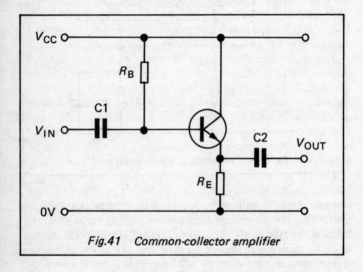

Fig.41   Common-collector amplifier

high current and power gain. The main applications of this amplifier stem from the fact that it has very high input impedance but low output impedance. Thus it requires very little current to drive it but is capable of generating a large output current. This makes it valuable as a link between a circuit with high output impedance and a circuit with low input impedance. Output is 0.6V below input and is in phase with it.

Design stages: the same as for the common-emitter amplifier (p.93), except that we select R_E to put the emitter voltage at $V_{CC}/2$.

Example: given that the supply voltage V_{CC} = 6V, and the transistor is a BC107 with typical gain 290 at 2mA. Minimum frequency to be passed is 100Hz. To obtain emitter voltage of 3.5V, R_E = 3/0.002 = 1500Ω. Use standard 1.5kΩ resistor. This gives a base voltage 3 + 0.6 = 3.6V. The voltage drop across R_B is 6 − 3.6 = 2.4. The base current is 2mA/h_{FE} = 0.002/290 = 6.9μA. Therefore the value of R_B is 2.4/(6.9 × 10^{-6}) = 348kΩ. Use a standard 330kΩ or 360kΩ resistor. We could instead bias the base with two resistors as in the common emitter amplifier. On the input side, f = 100Hz, C1 = $1/(2\pi fR)$ = $1/(2\pi \times 100 \times 330 \times 10^3)$ = 4.8 × 10^{-9}. Use a 4.7nF capacitor. On the output side, C2 = $1/(2\pi \times 100 \times 1.5 \times 10^3)$ = 1.1 × 10^{-6}. Use a 1μF capacitor.

The input impedance Z_{IN} of the transistor is $R_E.h_{FE}$. In the example given, Z_{IN} = 1.5 × 10^3 × 290 = 435kΩ. If this circuit is followed by another circuit with low input impedance, this is in parallel with R_E and the combined resistance of the two should be used in the above calculation. The input impedance of the transistor is in parallel with R_B, making the input impedance of the circuit as a whole: (435k × 330k)/(435k + 330k) = 188kΩ, which is high.

The output impedance Z_{OUT} of the transistor is R_B/h_{FE}. But R_B is in parallel with the output impedance of any previous stage to which the amplifier may be connected. If this is the low-noise amplifier of Figure 40, with Z_{OUT} = 10kΩ, their parallel resistance is (10k × 330k)/(10k + 330k) = 9.7kΩ. The output impedance of the previous stage is more important than the value of R_B at this stage. Now we calculate the output impedance of the transistor, 9700/290 = 33Ω. Output impedance is very low, a vital feature of this type of amplifier. If R_E has a low value (a few hundred ohms), the output can match a low-impedance device such as a loudspeaker, which can be connected directly between the V_{OUT} terminal and the 0V rail.

(iii) **Common base amplifier:** These amplifiers are characterised by high voltage and power gain, but a current gain of only 1 (Fig.42). Input impedance is low, while output impedance is high. There is no phase shift. The chief advantage of this amplifier is that the effect of collector-base capacitance at high frequencies (the Miller effect) is absent. This makes the

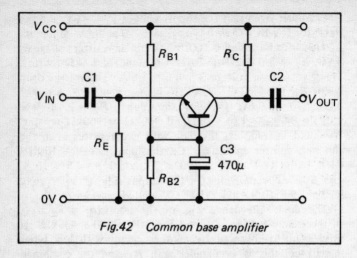

Fig.42   Common base amplifier

common base amplifier particularly suitable for radio frequency and very high frequency amplifiers.   In Figure 42 a by-pass capacitor C3 is used to pass a.c. signals to the 0V rail, so holding the base at a steady voltage.

Design stages: the same as for the common-emitter amplifier (p.93).

Example: given that the supply voltage V_{CC} = 9V, and the transistor is a BF180 with typical gain 100 at 10mA. Minimum frequency to be passed is 1kHz. To obtain collector voltage of 4.5V, R_C = 4.5/0.01 = 450Ω. Use standard 430Ω or 470Ω resistors. A suitable value for R_E is 1kΩ. Choose R_{B1} and R_{B2} to obtain the required base voltage 4.5 − 0.6 = 3.9V. In this example, we require a base current of 10mA/100 = 100μA, so the current through the resistors must be at least 10 times this, 1mA. The total value of the resistors must be no more than V_{CC}/I_B = 9/10^{-3} = 9kΩ. If the base voltage is to be 3.9V and V_{CC} = 9V, then the ratio $R_{B2}/(R_{B1} + R_{B2})$ is 3.9/9 = 0.43. R_{B2} = 0.43 × 9kΩ = 3.9kΩ. R_{B1} = 9kΩ − 3.9kΩ = 5.1kΩ. Check this selection using the formula on p.77. If this is not close enough, try using resistors of *lower* values to find a suitable combination of resistor using preferred (E12 or E24) values. On the input side, f = 1kHz, C1 = 1/(2πfR) = 1/(2π × 1000 × 1 × 10^3) = 159 × 10^{-9}.

Use a 150nF capacitor. On the output side, C2 = $1/(2\pi$
$\times 1000 \times 450) = 354 \times 10^{-9}$. Use a 470nF capacitor.

The input impedance of the transistor in this connection
is $25/I_E$, where I_E is expressed in milliamps. Thus Z_{IN} =
$25/10 = 2.5\Omega$. With such a low Z_{IN} the value of R_E is
ignored. The output impedance of the transistor is almost
infinite so only R_C has to be taken into account. Thus the
output impedance is 430Ω or 470Ω depending on the
resistor.

7 JFET amplifiers

There are three versions of these, comparable to the three
bipolar transistor amplifiers. The common gate amplifier is
rarely used except in a few high frequency applications, so it
is not described here. This section refers to amplifiers using
n-channel JFETs, which operate in the depletion mode.

(i) Common source amplifier: As can be seen from Figure
43, this is the JFET equivalent of the bipolar common emitter

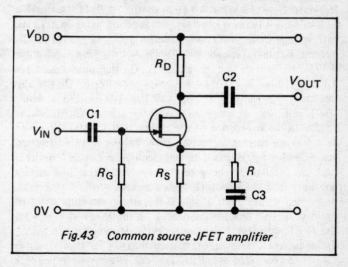

Fig.43   Common source JFET amplifier

amplifier. Its main advantage is the extremely high input
impedance, in the order of $1M\Omega$. Since the input current is
so small, the power gain is very high. It has a moderate voltage

gain, dependent on the size of the drain resistor. The relatively fast switching time of the transistor makes this type of amplifier suitable for radio frequencies. Noise levels are low. The main problem is that it is difficult to bias the transistor accurately, for individual transistors vary widely in their pinch-off point, the voltage (less than the gate voltage) at which the transistor turns off.

The design procedure is very similar to that for bipolar amplifiers. First decide on a suitable I_D and arrange that R_D drops half the supply voltage (V_{DD}). Select R_S so that the source voltage is sufficiently higher than the gate; if the transistor is to be turned off the source voltage must be higher than the pinch-off point. It will probably be necessary to include a trimmer resistor as part of R_S to allow for variations between transistors.

Example: Given that V_{DD} = 9V, and that frequencies above 100Hz are to be passed, take 0.5mA as a suitable I_D; note that this is considerably less than I_C for a bipolar transistor. R_D must have the value $4.5/(0.5 \times 10^{-3})$ = 9kΩ. A suitable E24 value is 9.1kΩ. R_G is 1MΩ, its function being to hold the gate voltage close to 0V, while source voltage depends on the current passing through R_S. With I_D = 0.5mA, and R_S = 4.7kΩ, the source voltage is 2.35V. On the input side, C1 = $1/(2\pi \times 100 \times 1 \times 10^6)$ = 1.6×10^{-9}, or 1.6nF. On the output side, C2 = $1/(2\pi \times 100 \times 9.1 \times 10^3)$ = 175×10^{-9}. Use 180nF.

The input impedance of the circuit is R_G, 1MΩ. However, gate leakage current increases appreciably at elevated temperatures, reducing the input impedance of the circuit. Another problem is that, if the gate-drain voltage exceeds a certain amount (the breakpoint), gate leakage current increases dramatically; the point at which this occurs depends upon the drain current. The situation may be improved by operating the JFET with less than the maximum drain voltage to reduce drain current. This unfortunately means that the transistor can not be operated over its full range. The output impedance is R_D, 9.1kΩ.

(ii) **Common drain amplifier:** This is also known as a *source follower* amplifier (Fig.44) and has the same function as the bipolar emitter follower (p.98). The voltage gain is theoretically 1 but may be as low as 0.9 in practice, so this amplifier

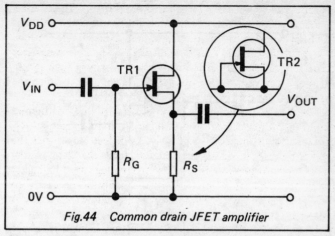

Fig.44   Common drain JFET amplifier

does not follow input voltage as closely as its bipolar counterpart. The input impedance equals R_G, (typically 1MΩ) which is very high. The output impedance is approximately equal to $1/g_m$. If g_m = 2mS (as in the case of the 2N3819 JFET), then Z_{OUT} for the transistor is 500Ω, which is low. The resistance of R_S (typically 4.7kΩ) is in parallel with this and can be ignored. Using a transistor such as the J109, with g_m = 10mS, gives Z_{OUT} of only 100Ω. There is zero phase shift with this amplifier. The values of R_S and the capacitors are calculated as in previous examples.

If R_S is replaced by a constant current device (another JFET; TR2 in Fig.44), which feeds its saturation current to the amplifying transistor, output is more linearly related to input. Output impedance is raised, which may be a disadvantage. In Figure 45, R_P programs TR2 to give less than its saturation current. R_G is connected to the drain of TR2 so that the voltage at its 'lower' end almost follows V_{IN}. Because of this, only a small current flows in R_G, which in effect has very low resistance. The result is a voltage follower with extremely high input impedance.

8 MOSFET amplifiers

With their rapid response time, low-power MOSFET amplifiers are widely used in radio frequency circuits. The high power

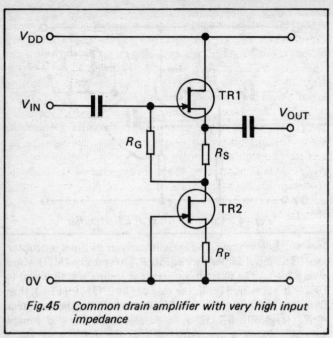

Fig.45 Common drain amplifier with very high input
impedance

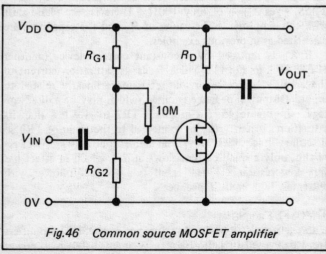

Fig.46 Common source MOSFET amplifier

gain of power MOSFETs, particularly those with VMOS construction, makes them popular in power-control circuits. Power MOSFETs have greater thermal stability than bipolar power transistors and are not subject to thermal runaway. They may be wired in parallel if necessary to allow control of large currents. It is essential to observe anti-static precautions when assembling circuits containing MOSFETs.

Figure 46 shows a common source MOSFET amplifier, using a n-channel enhancement mode MOSFET. The figure shows the gate biassed by two resistors R_{G1} and R_{G2}. In this respect the circuit is similar to Figure 39(c). Alternatively, R_{G1} can be connected to the drain terminal of the transistor (compare Fig.39(b)). Values of R_{G1} and R_{G2} are calculated as in the examples on pp.96 and 100 to provide a gate voltage that takes the transistor into its region of linear response. A suitable voltage is usually 2 or 3 volts above the threshold voltage V_{th}.

The input impedance of the circuit is the resistance of R_{G1} and R_{G2} in parallel. Since only a minute gate current is required, the values of these two resistors can be several hundred kilohms each, so the circuit has high input impedance. This can be raised even further by biasing the gate through the optional $10M\Omega$ resistor shown in the figure, giving a very high input impedance in excess of $10M\Omega$. The value of R_D and the capacitors are calculated as in previous examples.

9 Operational amplifier circuits

Figure 47 illustrates the most common uses of op amps. All the figures are based on a dual supply, the connections of which are not shown. The 0V rail shown in the figures is the middle supply rail. When single-supply op amps are used, the negative power input of the op amp may be connected to the 0V rail. The circuits work well with general purpose op amps such as the 741, TL081 or CA3140E. For improved performance, op amps with special features should be used with some of the circuits, as indicated below. Functions and details of the circuits of Figure 47 are as follows:

(a) **Non-inverting amplifier:** $V_{OUT} = V_{IN} \times (R_A + R_F)/R_A$. R_B may be omitted but for best performance make R_B equal

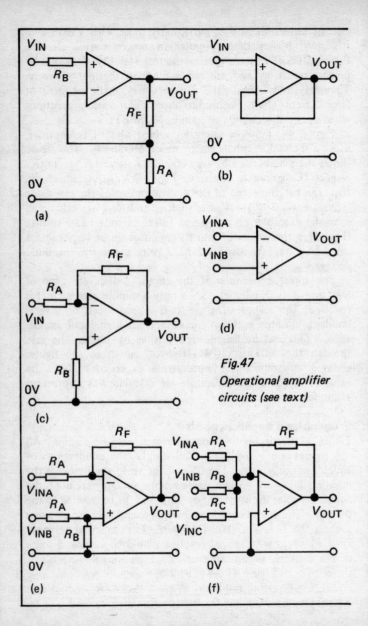

Fig.47
Operational amplifier
circuits (see text)

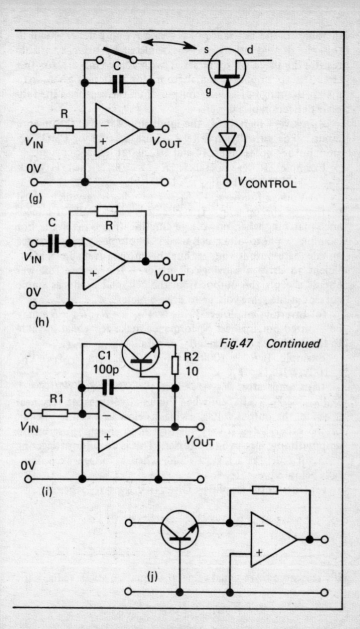

Fig.47 Continued

in value to the resistance of R_A and R_F in parallel. Gain in this circuit and others may be adjusted by using a variable resistor in place of or in series with R_F. One use for this circuit is to amplify a signal from (for example) a sensor to match the range of voltage output from the sensor to the full-scale deflection of a meter.

Z_{IN} is very high, being the input impedance of the op amp input. For virtually infinite Z_{IN}, use a JFET or CMOS op amp, but see notes on pp.44 and 102 about leakage current.

Example: If R_F = 100kΩ, R_A = 10kΩ, then V_{OUT} = $V_{IN} \times$ 110kΩ/10kΩ = $V_{IN} \times$ 11.

(b) Voltage follower: $V_{OUT} = V_{IN}$. Z_{IN} is very high, equal to that of the op amp. This circuit is often used for impedance matching when no voltage amplification is involved. For example, a photovoltaic cell used in photometry may produce an adequate output voltage, but the current available is insufficient to drive a moving-coil meter. The voltage follower circuit accepts the output from the cell, and produces ample current at the same voltage to drive a meter.

(c) Inverting amplifier: $V_{OUT} = V_{IN} \times -R_F/R_A$. R_B may be omitted but for best performance make R_B equal in value to the resistance of R_A and R_F in parallel. $Z_{IN} = R_A$.

Example: If R_F = 100kΩ, R_A = 10kΩ, then $V_{OUT} = V_{IN} \times$ 100kΩ/10kΩ = $V_{IN} \times -10$.

(d) Comparator: $V_{OUT} > 0$ if $V_{INB} > V_{INA}$. $V_{OUT} < 0$ if $V_{INB} < V_{INA}$. Except when the input voltages are very near in value, the output voltage swings as close as it can to one rail or the other. Z_{IN} is very high on both inputs. Use an op amp with low input voltage offset. This is useful for triggering a circuit (such as a logic circuit) when a voltage exceeds or falls below a preset level.

(e) Differential amplifier: Given that $R_B = R_F$, then

$$V_{OUT} = \frac{R_F \times (V_{INB} - V_{INA})}{R_A}$$

If all resistors are of equal value, the equation above reduces to:

$$V_{OUT} = V_{INB} - V_{INA}$$

108

In this form, the circuit is also known as a *subtractor*. Z_{IN} = R_A for V_{INA} and is $R_A + R_B$ for V_{INB}. The mis-matched impedances are a disadvantage of the circuit under certain circumstances. The circuit can be used to subtract an input offset voltage. For example, the output of the LM35Z temperature sensor (p.60) is proportional to temperature on the kelvin scale. At 0°C its output is 2.73V, and rises by 0.01V for every degree. To operate on the Celsius scale we need to subtract 2.73V from its output. If V_{INA} is held at 2.73V and V_{INB} is the output from the sensor, V_{OUT} is 0V at 0°C, rising by 0.01V for every degree rise in temperature. It goes negative for temperatures below zero. For greater resolution, make R_F and R_B larger than R_A so that the first equation applies. If for example $R_F/R_A = 100$, then V_{OUT} varies by 1V per degree.

(f) Summing amplifier: This is a current summing circuit so:

$$V_{OUT} = -R_F(V_{INA}/R_A + V_{INB}/R_B + V_{INC}/R_C)$$

The inputs are weighted by the resistors, the smaller the resistor the larger the weighting. This circuit is made use of as a digital to analogue converter (see p.249). If all resistors are of equal value, the equation above reduces to:

$$V_{OUT} = -(V_{INA} + V_{INB} + V_{INC})$$

The output is the negative of the sum of the inputs. Z_{IN} for each input equals the value of its input resistor.

Example: if all resistors are 10kΩ, $V_{INA} = 1.2$V, $V_{INB} = 0.6$V, and $V_{INC} = -0.3$V, then $V_{OUT} = -(1.2 + 0.6 + [-0.3]) = -1.5$V.

This circuit can be used as an audio mixer. It can be also used to subtract an offset voltage, as in the example above. Using the summer, one input is connected to the sensor, while the other is connected to a *negative* voltage of the required value.

(g) Integrator: Integrates the input voltage over a given period of time, from 0 to t seconds, with a scale factor of $-1/RC$:

$$V_{OUT} = \frac{-1}{RC} \int_0^t V_{IN}\,dt + k$$

where k is the initial value of V_{OUT}. The circuit is reset by closing the switch. This can be an FET or a CMOS analogue switch (p.194) if electronic resetting is required. Make $V_{CONTROL} = 0$ or positive to reset the ramp, make $V_{CONTROL}$ negative (= negative supply) to integrate. This circuit can be used as the basis of a *ramp generator*. In this application V_{IN} is a constant and, assuming $V_{OUT} = 0$ when t = 0:

$$V_{OUT} = -\frac{V_{IN}t}{RC}$$

Example: if V_{IN} is constant at 0.1V, R = 10kΩ, C = 10μF, t = 0.5s, and the initial V_{OUT} is 0V, then after 0.5s:

$$V_{OUT} = \frac{0.1 \times 0.5}{10 \times 10^3 \times 10 \times 10^{-6}} = 0.5V$$

Use an op amp with very low input offset voltage and low input current bias; JFET op amps are suitable. Another use for this circuit is to sum the changing value of a voltage over a period of time, for example to obtain a mean value, eliminating short-term variations.

(h) Differentiator:

$$V_{OUT} = -RC \times dV_{IN}/dt$$

The output depends on the *rate of change* of the input. This is useful for detecting short pulses or spikes of low amplitude. The actual amplitude of the spike may be very small but its rate of increase may be large in terms of volts per second, making V_{OUT} relatively large. Use an op amp with low noise and with high slew rate. The circuit can also be used for the more mathematical function of differentiating an analogue signal to convert it to an analogue of another physical quantity. For example, a signal representing the *position* of a moving object made by a position sensor is differentiated so that it represents the *velocity* of the object. This is because velocity is the *rate of change* of position. In mathematical terms $v = ds/dt$, where position is represented by variable s.

Example: the position of the object is represented by a voltage, ranging from 0V to 5V as its distance from a fixed point ranges from 0m to 5m. The distance of the object is increasing at 0.5m per second; $dV_{IN}/dt = 0.5$. Also given that $R = 1M\Omega$ and $C = 1\mu F$. While the object is moving, $V_{OUT} = -10 \times 10^6 \times 1 \times 10^{-6} \times 0.5 = -5$. V_{OUT} is proportional to dV_{IN}/dt at all stages of the object's motion. Although the input to the circuit is a measure of position, the output is an instant readout of velocity. Since the *acceleration* of the object is the rate of change of its velocity (acceleration = $d^2s/dt^2 \propto dV^2_{IN}/dt^2$), the output of the differentiator may be fed to a second differentiator to obtain an output proportional to acceleration.

(i) Logarithmic amplifier: The output of the amplifier is proportional to the logarithm of the input:

$$V_{OUT} = -k \times \log V_{IN} + c$$

where k is a constant proportional to the kelvin temperature and c is another constant proportional to R1 and the reverse leakage current of the transistor. R2 and C1 are intended to stabilise the amplifier; the figure shows suggested values. The output of several such amplifiers each with identical transistors at the same temperature (e.g. a transistor array) can be summed using circuit (f). Adding logarithms of two or more values gives the logarithm of their *product*, so this is a technique for multiplying two values together.

To obtain the final result the output from the mixer is passed to the anti-logarithmic amplifier, shown at (j). Division can be accomplished in circuits of this type by subtracting inputs. Note that the logarithm of zero and of negative values are not mathematically meaningful; only positive voltages give a valid result when input to a logarithmic amplifier. Although a reasonably reliable result can be obtained by using precision op amps, it is preferable to use an ic which includes the transistor and other components in a ready-made log-antilog amplifier. An example is the SSM2100P, which contains two such amplifiers. An alternative is an *analogue multiplier*. A device of this kind can accept up to three varying inputs, and multiply, divide, square or square-root them in various combinations. It can also multiply the result by a constant factor. Examples are the SG1495N (inexpensive), the MPY634KP (high bandwidth) and the AD534JH (precision).

Precision voltage reference

This circuit (Fig.48) allows reference voltages to be obtained that are not available from standard Zener diodes (p.32) or bandgap references (p.42). Further, it makes it possible to use Zeners in the range 5.6V to 6.2V. Zeners in this range have the least slope resistance and the lowest tempco. The values of the resistors are calculated as follows, assuming a current of 5mA through the Zener or bandgap reference:

$$R1 = 200 \times (V_{OUT} - V_Z)$$
$$R2 = 1000 \times (V_{OUT} - V_Z)$$
$$R3 = 1000 \times V_Z$$

It is essential to ensure that the output is capable of swinging to the voltage required.

Example: V_Z = 5.6V. To obtain V_{OUT} = 8.0V, R1 = 200 × 2.4 = 480Ω; R2 = 1000 × 2.4 = 2.4kΩ; R3 = 1000 × 5.6 = 5.6kΩ. For R1 use two 240Ω resistors in series.

More op amp circuits

See sections 11 *Precision rectifiers*, 12 *Peak voltage detectors*, 13 *Sample and hold circuits*, and 14 *Filters*.

Interfacing op amps to logic

There are few problems if the op amp and logic ic operate with the same supply voltage, provided that the slew rate of the amplifier is fast enough to present a clean 'edge' to the logic input. CMOS and JFET op amps are better in this respect. If the op amp and logic operate on different supply levels it is

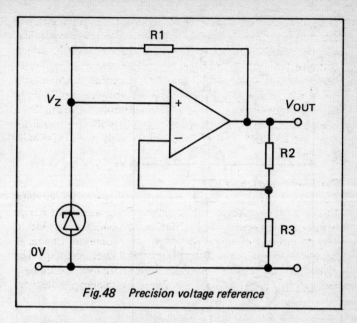

Fig.48   Precision voltage reference

necessary to limit the output swing of the op amp by clamping it, as in Figure 49. The silicon diodes clamp the output between −0.6V and +5.6V. Alternatively omit D1 and replace D2 with a 4.7V Zener. This clamps the output between −0.6V and +4.7V.

10 Comparator circuits

An op amp may be used as a comparator (p.108) but better performance is obtained by using an ic specially intended for this function. Figure 50 shows a basic comparator circuit. A comparator normally has an open-collector output so a pull-up resistor (typically 1kΩ) is required. The pull-up resistor can be connected to a voltage higher than the positive supply to the comparator. The reference voltage is provided either by a potential divider (p.77, usually a variable one as in Fig.23), a Zener diode (p.32) or a bandgap voltage reference (p.42). V_{IN} and V_{REF} can lie between +V and −V. Output is 0V when $V_{IN} < V_{REF}$ and is +V when $V_{IN} > V_{REF}$. Input impedance varies as the output changes state; feed the input

113

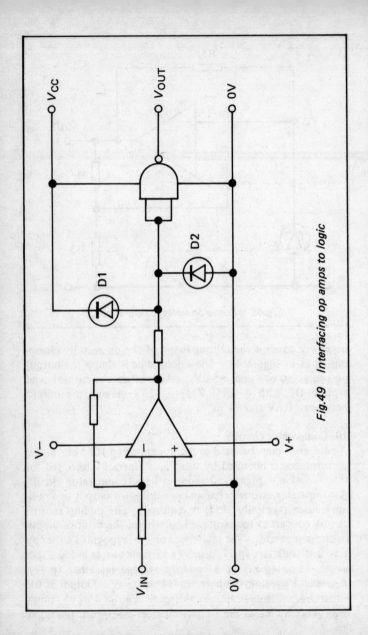

Fig.49 Interfacing op amps to logic

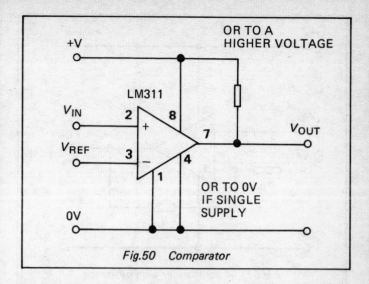

Fig.50 Comparator

from a low impedance source. Comparators are often used for interfacing analogue outputs to digital inputs.

If V_{IN} changes slowly the output of the comparator may show considerable jitter. This may be avoided by introducing hysteresis, as in Figure 51. Note that feedback is *positive*, so V_{REF} is connected to the (+) input and the action is the reverse of that described for Figure 50. The hysteresis Δ is given by:

$$\Delta = \frac{R_B}{R_A} + R_B \times V_{SWING}$$

where V_{SWING} is the difference between the high and low output voltages.

The output of the window discriminator (Fig.52) is high (+V) when V_{IN} lies between two fixed voltages (i.e. is in the 'window'). The voltages are set by the potential divider network consisting of R_A, R_B and R_C. Calculate the resistor values as in the following example.

Example: Decide on a suitable value for the total resistance R_T. Let this be 10kΩ. Given supply voltage $V_S = 6V$ and

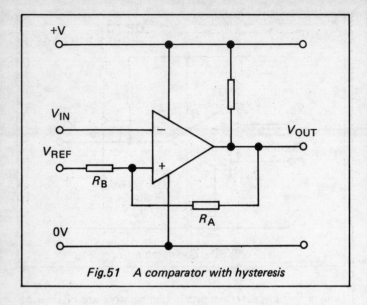

Fig.51   A comparator with hysteresis

that V_A is to be 3V and V_B is to be 2V.

$$R_A = (V_S - V_A) \times R_T/V_S = 5k\Omega$$
$$R_B = (V_A - V_B) \times R_T/V_S = 1.7k\Omega$$
$$R_C = V_B \times R_T/V_S = 3.3k\Omega$$

11 Precision rectifiers

If an a.c. signal has to be converted into d.c., it can be rectified using a 4-diode bridge (p.306) but this results in a loss of the forward voltage drop of the diodes. If the signal voltage is small, this loss can be serious and introduce severe distortion at the crossover points.

The half-wave op amp precision rectifier (Fig.53) is not subject to such errors, but must take its input from a low-impedance source and deliver it to a high impedance. The full-wave version requires two op amps (Fig.54). The only significant error in the output is due to offset input voltages. In the half-wave rectifier the error equals the offset voltage. In the full-wave rectifier, error is equal to twice the offset of

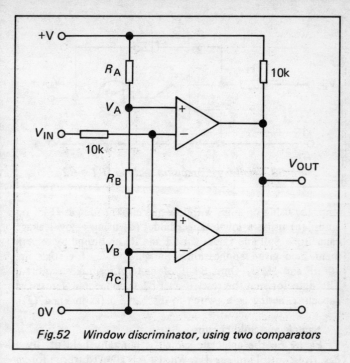

Fig.52   Window discriminator, using two comparators

the first amplifier plus that of the second amplifier, i.e. a total of three times the input offset, if amplifiers are identical. This gives a total of 10–15mV for CMOS and JFET amplifiers and about half this for bipolar amplifiers. The error can be reduced by offset nulling, or by using an amplifier such as the OP-27G with offset of only 30μV, giving a total error of approximately 0.1mV for the full-wave rectifier.

12 Peak voltage detectors

The circuit in Figure 55 uses a precision rectifier to charge a capacitor to the peak positive voltage attained by the input. The high-value resistor allows the capacitor to discharge slowly.   Together the resistor and capacitor act as a 'memory' storing the most recent peak value for a limited period of time. Output 'droops' as current leaks away from the capacitor. This is minimised by (a) feeding the output to a voltage-follower op

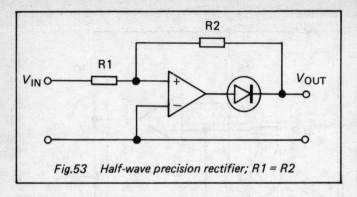

Fig.53   Half-wave precision rectifier; R1 = R2

amp; (b) using op amps with low bias current such as JFET op amps; (c) using a low-leakage diode; (d) using a low-leakage capacitor. Suitable values for C1 and R1 are found by experiment in a given application. Suitable values for trials are 100nF and 1MΩ. Omit R1 if a long-term reading is required. The detector may be reset if an FET is connected across the capacitor, acting as a switch to discharge it (as in Fig.47(g)).

13 Sample and hold circuits

In Figure 56 the analogue switch is normally held off by a negative control voltage V_C. When V_C is allowed to rise for an instant the switch is turned on and the voltage across C is a sample of V_{IN}. The op amp is used as a voltage follower; it has very high impedance so that the charge is held on C for a relatively long time. It will leak away eventually but, to minimise loss of charge between samplings ('droop'), use a low leakage capacitor such as polypropylene. Also use an op amp with low bias current, such as a JFET type. The larger the value of C the lower the effects of leakage but the longer the capacitor takes to acquire the new value of V_{IN}. If the capacitor starts from zero charge, it reaches 99% of its maximum charge in 5RC seconds, where R is the resistance of the switch. The resistance of a 4016 analogue switch is 250Ω when operated on a ±5V supply. If C = 100nF the capacitor reaches full charge in $5 \times 250 \times 100 \times 10^{-9} = 125\mu s$. If lower precision is required, the calculation can be based on it reaching 98% of its maximum charge in 4RC seconds. For shorter

118

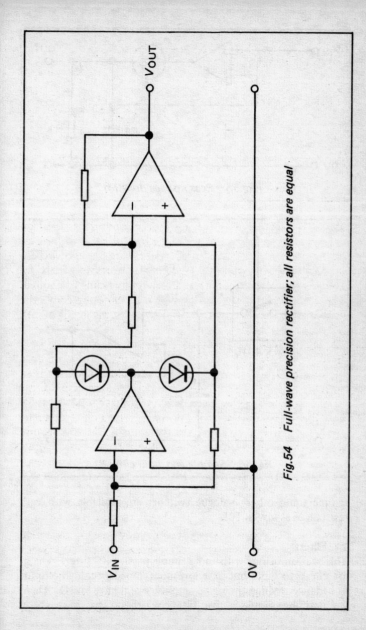

Fig.54 Full-wave precision rectifier; all resistors are equal.

119

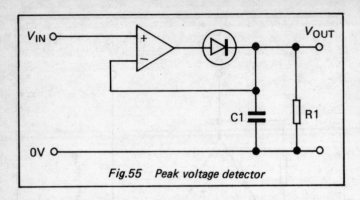

Fig.55 Peak voltage detector

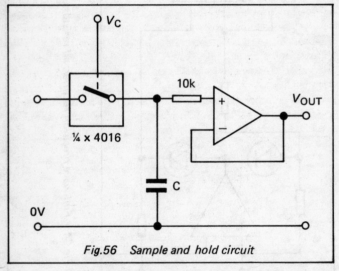

Fig.56 Sample and hold circuit

sample times other analogue switches are available with 'on' resistances as low as 10Ω.

14 Filters

This section begins with some simple passive RC filters, which are cheap to build but have low input impedance, high output impedance, reduce the signal amplitude and have low Q. Then we describe simple active filters which do not have these drawbacks, based on op amps. Finally we describe a range of filters of other types suited to specific purposes. Radio-frequency filters are described in Chapter 7. A more comprehensive approach to filter design is given in BP299, *Practical Electronic Filters*.

Passive RC filters

The basic low-pass filter and high-pass filter (Fig.57) have a cut-off frequency (the −3dB point) given by:

$$f_C = 1/2\pi RC = 0.16/RC$$

The roll-off in the stop-band is 6dB per octave. The phase lag φ of the low-pass filter is −45°C at the cut-off frequency, less (approaching 0°) at lower frequencies and more (approaching −90°) at higher frequencies. For the high-pass filter there is a phase *lead* of 45° at f_C. This approaches +90° at lower frequencies and decreases toward zero at higher frequencies.

Two or more first-order filters as described above may be cascaded to give second-order and higher-order filters (Fig.58).

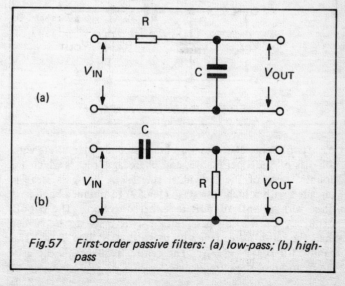

Fig.57   First-order passive filters: (a) low-pass; (b) high-pass

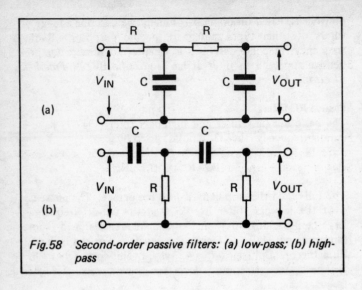

Fig.58   Second-order passive filters: (a) low-pass; (b) high-pass

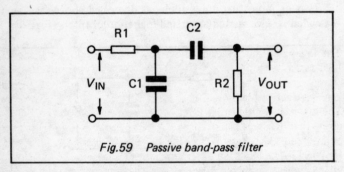

Fig.59   Passive band-pass filter

With two identical stages we obtain second-order filters with roll-offs of 12dB per octave, and phase lags or leads which are double those of the individual stages. A low-pass stage is cascaded with a high-pass stage (Fig.59) to obtain a band-pass filter with roll-off of 6dB in either direction. The cut-off frequency of the low-pass filter f_{CL} is made to be higher than the cut-off frequency of the high-pass filter f_{CH}. The bandwidth is $f_{CL} - f_{CH}$. The centre frequency is the geometric mean of these frequencies:

$$f_0 = \sqrt{f_{CL} \times f_{CH}}$$

Given the bandwidth BW and the centre frequency, f_{CL} is calculated from:

$$f_{CL} = \frac{BW + \sqrt{(BW^2 + 4 \times f_0{}^2)}}{2}$$

Examples:

(1) Design a low-pass filter with cut-off point at 10kHz. Select a possible capacitor value, say 1nF. Then:

$$R = 0.16/Cf_C = 16k\Omega$$

(2) Design a band-pass filter, bandwidth 1kHz with $f_0 = $ 15kHz.

$$f_{CL} = \frac{1000 + \sqrt{(1000 \times 1000 + 4 \times 15000^2)}}{2} = 15508Hz$$

$$f_{CH} = 15508 - 1000 = 14508Hz$$

The low-pass filter is designed for $f_{CL} = $ 15.508kHz and the high-pass filter for $f_{CH} = $ 14.508kHz.

Low-pass active filters

The low-pass second-order filter of Figure 60 has $f_C = 0.16/RC$ given that R1 = R2 and C1 = C2. The roll-off is 12dB per octave and the phase lag at the cut-off frequency is $-90°$.

The feedback of the filter introduces controlled damping which, with a suitable choice of gain, determine the response of the filter. Here we describe how to obtain the Butterworth response, one of the more generally useful types of filter. This has a flat pass-band and a reasonably sharp fall-off around the cut-off frequency — sharper than for the simple passive filter already described. Other responses include Bessel and Chebyshev, which are dealt with in the book referred to above.

Damping is controlled by varying the gain A of the amplifier:

$$A = \frac{R3 + R4}{R4}$$

123

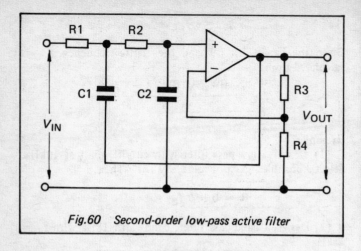

Fig.60   Second-order low-pass active filter

For the Butterworth response, A must be equal to 1.59. To design the filter, first decide on a capacitor value, then calculate the resistance, using $R = 0.16/Cf_C$. Calculate suitable values for the damping resistors by first selecting a value for R4, then calculating a value of R3 to produce the required amplification:

$$R3 = R4(A - 1) = R4 \times 0.59$$

It is important that the amplification is not allowed to approach 3, for this makes Q large and the circuit is liable to oscillate.

Example: Design a 2nd-order active low-pass filter with Butterworth response and cut-off point at 50Hz. Obviously a fairly large capacitance is required. Try 220nF capacitors, which would require $R1 = R2 = 0.16/(220 \times 10^{-9} \times 50) = 14.5k\Omega$. Decide on $39k\Omega$ for R4, then $R3 = R4 \times 0.59 = 39k\Omega \times 0.59 = 23.01k\Omega$. A $24k\Omega$ resistor is the nearest E24 value, but the more readily available $22k\Omega$ resistor could equally well be used, if only ±5% tolerance is provided by the capacitor.

Two 2nd-order filters are cascaded to produce a 4th-order filter with a roll-off of −24dB (Fig.61). The cut-off frequency

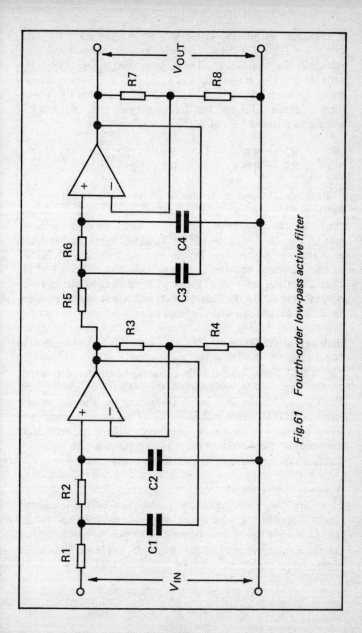

Fig.61   Fourth-order low-pass active filter

125

is calculated as before, where R = R1 = R2 = R5 = R6, and C = C1 = C2 = C3 = C4. Decide on a capacitor value and calculate the resistance. The gain is distributed unequally between the two stages; gains of 1.152 and 2.235 respectively, giving an overall gain of $1.152 \times 2.235 = 2.6$ for the whole filter. Calculate R3 and R4 to obtain a gain of 1.152, and R7 and R8 to obtain a gain of 2.235:

$$R3 = R4(A_1 - 1) = R4 \times 0.152$$
$$R7 = R8(A_2 - 1) = R8 \times 1.235$$

Example: Design a 4th-order active low-pass filter with Butterworth response and cut-off point at 5kHz. Select 10nF as the capacitor value for both sections. R = $0.16/(10 \times 10^{-9} \times 5 \times 10^3) = 3.2k\Omega$. Use an E12 resistor of 3.3kΩ, or a precision E96 resistor of 3.16kΩ or 3.24kΩ. In the damping equations, assume that R4 = R8 = 39kΩ. Then calculate R3 = 39k$\Omega \times 0.152 = 5.9k\Omega$. Calculate R7 = 39k$\Omega \times 1.235 = 48.2k\Omega$. 5.6k$\Omega$ and 47kΩ resistors would be close enough for a low-precision filter.

High-pass active filters
The circuit for the 2nd-order high-pass active filter is shown in Figure 62. The 4th-order filter consists of two cascaded filters of this type. The response of these filters at the highest frequencies in the pass-band is limited by the frequency response of the operational amplifier. Thus an active high-pass filter is really a band-pass filter with roll-off at very high frequency. The procedure for designing Butterworth high-pass filters is exactly the same as that for low-pass filters.

Band-pass active filters
There are two main approaches, depending on the fractional bandwidth required, where fractional bandwidth = bandwidth/f_0. Given the lower and upper cut-off points, f_{CL} and f_{CH}, calculate the bandwidth, BW = $f_{CH} - f_{CL}$. Then calculate the centre frequency:

$$f_0 = \sqrt{(f_{CL} \times f_{CH})}$$

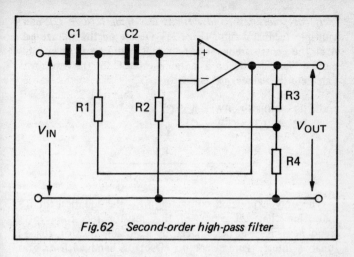

Fig.62   Second-order high-pass filter

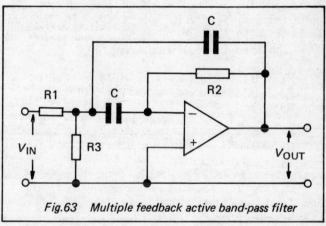

Fig.63   Multiple feedback active band-pass filter

Finally, calculate the fractional bandwidth = BW/f_0. Given the centre frequency f_0 and Q, we calculate the fractional bandwidth directly as $1/Q$.

If the fractional bandwidth is more than 1, design a low-pass filter with cut-off frequency f_{CH}, and a high-pass filter with cut-off frequency f_{CL}, as described in the sections above. Connect the filters in cascade.

If the fractional bandwidth is less than 1 (high Q), use a multiple feedback filter (Fig.63). Decide on the voltage gain A at the centre frequency, f_0. This could be 1, or possibly more. Next decide on a suitable value C for the capacitors. Calculate the values of the resistors:

$$R1 = 0.159/(BW \times A \times C)$$
$$R2 = 0.318/(BW \times C)$$

$$R3 = \frac{R1}{(39.5 \times f_0^2 \times C^2 \times R1 \times R2) - 1}$$

The only expression containing f_0 is the equation for R3, indicating that the value of this resistor sets the central frequency. R3 can be replaced by a variable resistor, giving a tunable filter. Tuning has no effect on bandwidth or gain.

Example: Design a band-pass filter, bandwidth = 250Hz, centre frequency f_0 = 2kHz, gain A = 4. The fractional bandwidth is $250/2000 = 0.125$, we design a multiple feedback filter. The capacitor value is selected as 4.7nF.

$$R1 = 0.159/(250 \times 4 \times 4.7 \times 10^{-9}) = 33.8k\Omega$$
$$R2 = 0.318/(250 \times 4.7 \times 10^{-9}) = 270k\Omega$$
$$R3 =$$

$$\frac{33.8 \times 10^3}{(39.5 \times 2000^2 \times (4.7 \times 10^{-9})^2 \times 33.8 \times 10^3 \times 270 \times 10^3) - 1}$$

$$= 1092\Omega.$$

Suitable values are 33kΩ, 270kΩ, and 1.1kΩ.

A 4th-order band-pass filter is built from two cascaded 2nd-order filters. It has a relatively wider pass band combined with steeper roll-off on either side. The filters are designed with equal Q but their central frequencies are staggered by a factor *a*, which usually has a value in the range 1.005 (pass-band only slightly wider than the 2nd-order filter) to 2.0 (broad flat pass-band). If f_0 is the required central frequency, design the filters as above, with central frequencies f_0/a and $f_0 \times a$, respectively.

Notch filters

One method of obtaining a notch filter is to sum the low-pass and high-pass outputs of a state-variable filter (see next section). The circuit in Figure 64 shows a notch filter that can be built as a fixed-frequency filter or as a tunable filter.

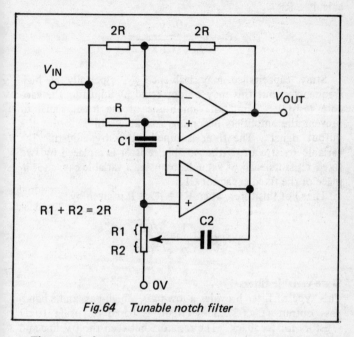

Fig.64   Tunable notch filter

The notch frequency depends on the values of the capacitors and the setting of the variable resistor. Suitable values for the resistors marked R and 2R are 100kΩ and 200kΩ, though R can have any value between 47kΩ and 1MΩ. C1 should be in the range 100pF to 39nF, and C2 should lie between 100nF and 10μF. The variable resistor is considered as being divided at its wiper position into two sections, R1 and R2. The notch frequency is:

$$f_0 = \frac{1}{2\pi\sqrt{C1 \times C2 \times R1 \times R2}}$$

If the variable resistor is replaced by two fixed resistors, each of value R, frequency may be adjusted by making C1 a variable capacitor.

To design the filter, first decide on values for C1 and C2; C1 = 2.2nF and C2 = 1μF are suitable starting values. Then calculate R:

$$R = \frac{0.16}{f_0 \sqrt{(C1 \times C2)}}$$

Stray capacitance may influence f_0, especially at high frequencies, but this may be corrected by adjusting the variable resistor. Limit the amplitude of the input signal to prevent the amplifiers becoming saturated and distorting the output signal. The filter is tuned either by adjusting the variable resistor or, if the variable resistor is replaced by two fixed resistors each of value R, by using a variable capacitor in place of the fixed capacitor C1.

The Q of this filter, when R1 = R2 = R is given by:

$$Q = \frac{1}{2} \sqrt{\frac{C2}{C1}}$$

State-variable filters

This type of filter provides a low-pass, a high-pass and a band-pass output (Fig.65). This circuit is based on using 10kΩ resistors for feedback. The resistors between the 0V line and the (+) inputs of the amplifiers can be replaced by short-circuits to 0V in non-critical applications.

Calculate the values of R1 to R4:

R2 and R3 determine f_0, where R2 = R3 = R = $0.16/Cf_0$.

R4 determines Q, where R4 = 10kΩ × Q.

Given the required gain A, calculate the value of R1 = R4/A.

Variable resistors (ganged in the case of R2 and R3) are used if variable gain, frequency or Q are required.

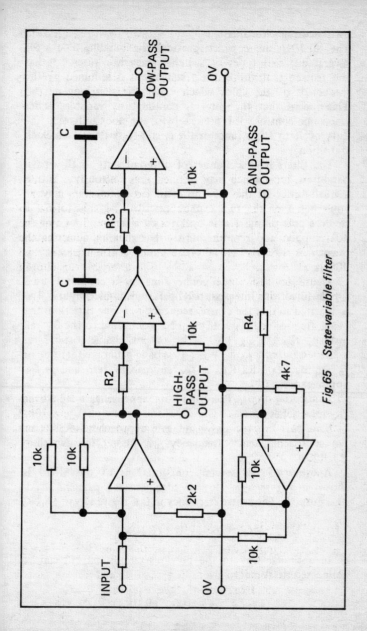

Fig.65   State-variable filter

LOW-PASS OUTPUT

0V

BAND-PASS OUTPUT

C

R3

10k

C

R2

10k

R4

HIGH-PASS OUTPUT

4k7

10k

10k

10k

2k2

10k

INPUT

0V

131

Switched capacitor filters

The MF10 is an ic which provides the building blocks for several different types of switched capacitor filter. It has the feature that the centre frequency is determined by the frequency of the clock which drives the switching circuit. This means that the filter is continuously variable, under electronic control. It is preferable for the clock to have a 50% duty cycle to allow time for the circuit to settle at each clock transition.

The filters have a number of different outputs (low-pass, band-pass, etc.) which may be used simultaneously. This is a dual device so that two different two-pole filters may be constructed or the two can be cascaded together to give a single 4-pole filter. The ic operates on a dual ±5V or a single 10V supply, and requires 8mA. The maximum clock frequency is 1.5MHz and the maximum centre frequency is 30kHz.

Figure 66 shows the connections for a commonly-used 2-pole filter with low-pass, band-pass and notch outputs. The ic is wired so that the centre frequency f_0 is one-fiftieth of the clock frequency f_{CLK}. If pin 12 is connected to the 0V rail instead, $f_0 = f_{CLK}/100$. The output characteristics are:

Notch output: $f_{notch} = f_0$. Pass band gain on either side of f_0 approaches $-R2/R1$, as f_{IN} approaches zero and as f_{IN} approaches $f_{CLK}/2$.

Low-pass output: Pass-band gain approaches $-R2/R1$ as f_{IN} approaches zero.

Band-pass output: Pass-band gain approaches $-R3/R1$ as f_{IN} approaches centre frequency f_0. $Q = f_0/$bandwidth = $R3/R2$.

Another of the several configurations of the MF10 is shown in Figure 67. This has high-pass, low-pass and band-pass outputs. The centre frequency in this is given by:

$$f_0 = f_{CLK}/50 \times (R2/R4)$$

In a similar way to the previous circuit, pin 12 can be connected to 0V rail to give:

$$f_0 = f_{CLK}/100 \times (R2/R4)$$

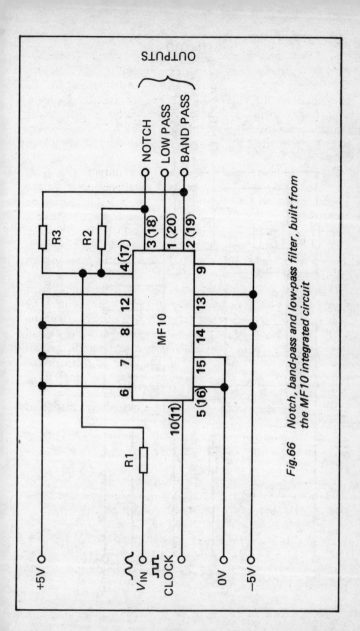

Fig.66 Notch, band-pass and low-pass filter, built from the MF10 integrated circuit

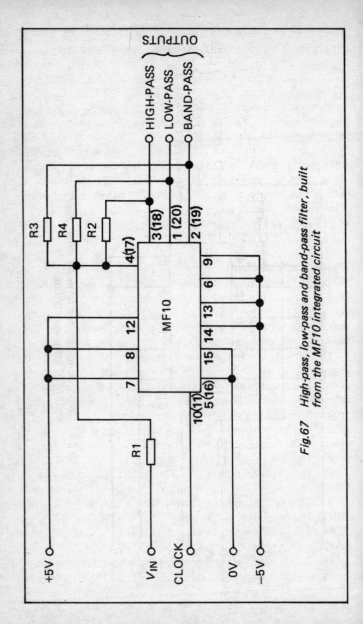

Fig.67   High-pass, low-pass and band-pass filter, built
from the MF10 integrated circuit

134

The output characteristics are:

High-pass output: Pass-band gain approaches $-R2/R1$ as f_{IN} approaches $f_{CLK}/2$.

Low-pass output: Pass-band gain approaches $-R4/R1$ as f_{IN} approaches zero.

Band-pass output: Bass-band gain approaches $-R3/R1$ as f_{IN} approaches f_0. $Q = R3/R2 \times (R2/R4)$.

In both circuits pin 9 must be connected to as to adjust voltage levels to the levels of the clock. As shown, pin 9 is connected to $-5V$, which is correct for use with a CMOS clock when the power supply is $\pm 5V$. If a TTL clock is used with a $\pm 5V$ supply, connect pin 9 to 0V. When using a single 10V supply, connect pins 13 and 14 to 0V, and pin 15 to $+5V$ (i.e. midway between 0V and 10V). Connect pin 9 to 0V for CMOS or TTL clocks.

Digital band-pass filter

Although this is a digital circuit (Fig.68), built from a decidedly digital ic, and intended to filter digital signals, it belongs in the analogue section. This is reasonable, given that filtering depends on *frequency* which is an analogue quantity in the time domain, even though the voltage levels may be digital.

The circuit consists of two monostable vibrators (p.214) connected so as to be positive-edge triggered and retriggerable. The timing resistor and capacitor for each monostable determine the cut-off frequencies, f_1 and f_2. Calculate the required timing periods for the monostables: $t_1 = 1/f_1$ and $t_2 = 1/f_2$, given that $t_1 > t_2$. Then calculate the required values of the timing resistors and capacitors:

For the 4098, $t_1 = 0.5(R1 \times C1)$ and $t_2 = 0.5(R2 \times C2)$.

For the 74HC4058, $t_1 = 0.7(R1 \times C1)$ and $t_2 = 0.7(R2 \times C2)$.

With the 4098, resistors should be in the range $5k\Omega$ to $10M\Omega$ and capacitors in the range 10nF to $100\mu F$. With the 74HC4058, the minimum resistor value is $1.4k\Omega$ and the maximum capacitor value is $1\mu F$.

The period of the input signal is taken as $t_3 = 1/f_3$.

The circuit responds differently to the three possible conditions:

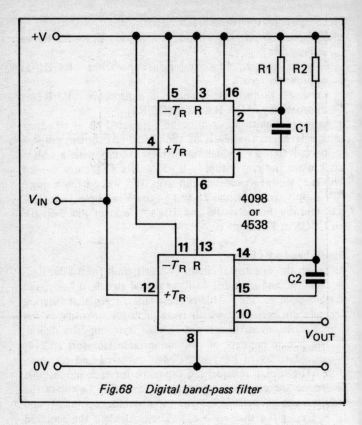

Fig.68 Digital band-pass filter

Frequency *above* range ($t_1 > t_2 > t_3$): output is continuously high.

Frequency *within* range ($t_1 > t_3 > t_2$): output is a train of pulses, frequency f_3.

Frequency *below* range ($t_3 > t_1 > t_2$): output is continuously low.

15 Audio circuits

Audio amplifiers

The simple circuits of Figures 39, 40, 43, 46, 47(a) and 47(c) are suitable for use in audio applications, used either

136

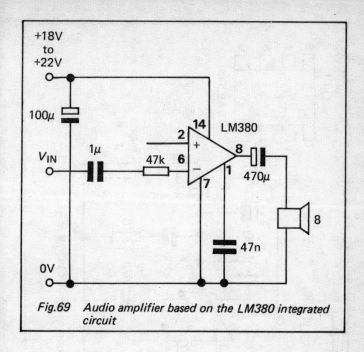

Fig.69   Audio amplifier based on the LM380 integrated circuit

on their own as low-power amplifiers, or as pre-amplifiers to be followed by one of the ic's described below. Figure 47(f) is used as an audio signal mixer and may also provide a certain amount of amplification. There are a number of ic's designed specifically as audio amplifiers. Three of the most useful of these are the LM380, the TBA820M and the TDA2030. Typical application circuits are shown below.

LM380 (Fig.69): A 2W amplifier (0.2% distortion) which requires the minimum of external components. It has a 14-pin d.i.l. package, pins 3–5 and 10–12 being connected to ground. These pins are soldered to a large area (approx. 40cm^2) of copper on the pcb to act as a heat sink. Input impedance is 150kΩ and the quiescent supply current is 7mA. Maximum power dissipation is 10W with a clip-on or glue-on heatsink (12°C/W).

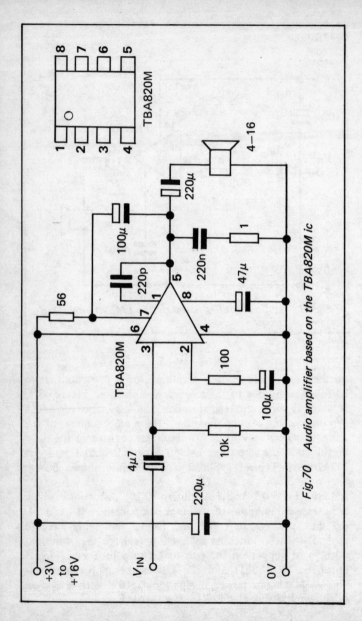

Fig.70   Audio amplifier based on the TBA820M ic

138

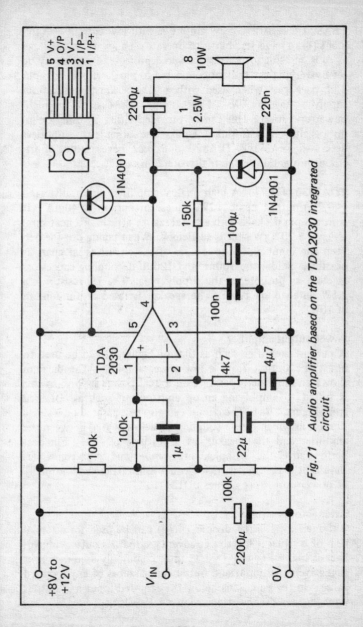

Fig.71   Audio amplifier based on the TDA2030 integrated
circuit

139

TBA820 (Fig.70): A 2W amplifier with low current requirement (4mA) and its ability to operate on a low supply voltage (3V) is an asset for battery-powered projects. Its gain may be set by varying the resistor connected to pin 2. It is in an 8-pin d.i.l. package. When used with a 4Ω speaker the maximum supply voltage is 9V. Heat-sinking is necessary for high-power operation. This can be provided either by using a clip-on or glue-on heat sink. Unlike the other two amplifiers described here, the TBA820 does *not* have output short-circuit protection or thermal protection.

TDA2030 (Fig.71): A high quality amplifier with undistorted (<0.2%) output up to 12W. Quiescent current is 40mA. It is in a 5-pin package with a metal tag for attaching a heat sink. Usually a 20$°$C/W sink is sufficient. When laying out the pcb keep the input and output sides of the circuit as far apart as possible. Solder the 100nF and 100μF decoupling capacitors as close as possible to the supply pins. The 1Ω resistor is a 2.5W wire-wound type. The speaker is rated at a minimum of 10W.

Power output amplifier

A current amplifier such as that of Figure 72 can be used to boost the output from a low-power amplifier. The diagram shows an amplifier operating on a dual power supply, so this is suited to amplifying an op amp output such as obtained from Figure 47(a). The circuit can also be operated on a single supply, in which case a coupling capacitor is used between the amplifier and the speaker, as in Figures 69–71. For best performance the complementary *npn* and *pnp* transistors should be a pair matched for equal gain. These will normally be power transistors such as BD131/132.

Attenuator networks

Although a potential divider (p.77) can be used for attenuation of a signal it has the disadvantage that its output impedance is high. Figure 73 shows three commonly used networks that have equal input and output impedances of any required value. In the equations below the required input and output impedance is Z. The attenuation $a = V_{IN}/V_{OUT}$.

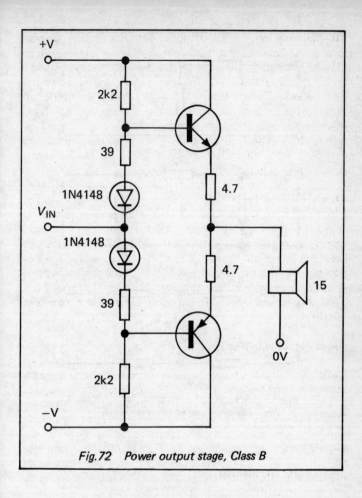

Fig.72   Power output stage, Class B

T-network: Unbalanced.

$$R_A = Z \times \frac{(a-1)}{(a+1)} \qquad R_B = Z \times \frac{2a}{(a^2-1)}$$

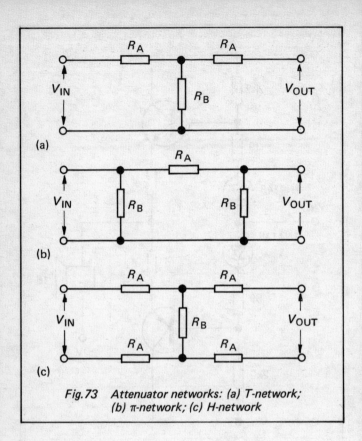

Fig.73   Attenuator networks: (a) T-network;
(b) π-network; (c) H-network

π-network: Unbalanced.

$$R_A = Z \times \frac{(a^2 - 1)}{2a} \qquad R_B = Z \times \frac{(a + 1)}{(a - 1)}$$

H-network: Balanced.

$$R_A = Z \times \frac{(a - 1)}{2(a + 1)} \qquad R_B = Z \times \frac{2a}{(a^2 - 1)}$$

Attenuators may be cascaded to obtain greater attenuation. If the attenuation of the individual stages are $a_1, a_2, \ldots$, etc., that of the chain is $a_1 \times a_2 \times \ldots$ etc.

Voltage controlled attenuator

The circuit of Figure 74 provides a reasonably linear control. As the control voltage is increased, the JFET is turned more fully on and a greater proportion of the signal is short-circuited to the 0V rail.

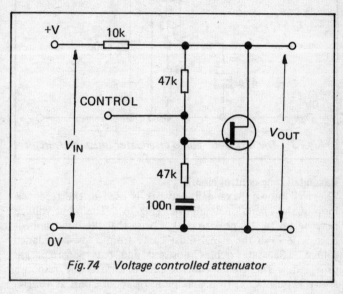

Fig.74   Voltage controlled attenuator

Attenuator integrated circuit

The MC3340P (Fig.75) is a voltage-controlled attenuator for audio signals up to 1MHz. The gain control range is +13dB to −90dB. Gain is set either by adjusting the variable resistor over the range 4kΩ to 33kΩ, or by applying a control voltage in the range 3.5V to 6V directly to pin 2 (omitting the variable resistor). Maximum input is 500mV r.m.s., impedance 17kΩ. Maximum output is 2.8V r.m.s., impedance 260Ω. The device is in an 8-pin d.i.l. package with no connections to pins 4 or 5.

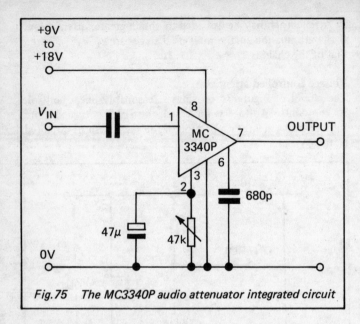

Fig.75   The MC3340P audio attenuator integrated circuit

Baxandall tone-control circuit

The well-known Baxandall network is used in the feedback loop of the operational amplifier (Fig.76). The input voltage may be up to 2V peak-to-peak. Note that the input impedance is low, so the signal must come from a low-impedance source. Separate treble boost/cut and bass boost/cut are provided. The treble control cuts or boosts the response above about 1kHz, to a maximum of about 20dB at 10kHz. Similarly, the bass control cuts or boosts the response below 1kHz, to a maximum of about 20dB at about 50Hz. The response may be altered by substituting other values for R4 and R5.

16 Impedance matching

The impedance (Z) of a circuit, expressed in ohms, may consist of two parts, resistance (R) and reactance (X), also expressed in ohms. Reactance may consist of two parts, capacitive reactance (X_C) and inductive reactance (X_L). Resistance is independent of frequency but both types of

144

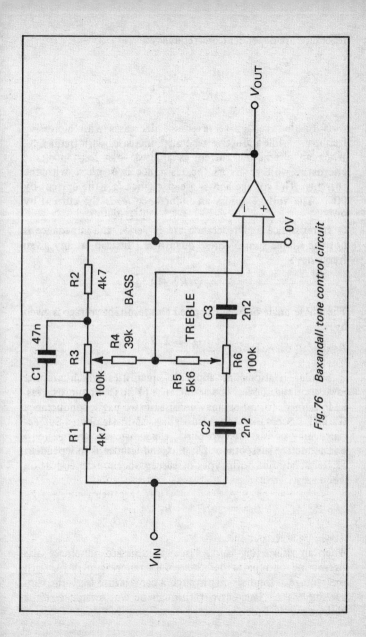

Fig. 76   Baxandall tone control circuit

reactance are dependent on frequency:

$$X_C = \frac{1}{2\pi f C} \qquad X_L = 2\pi f L$$

Note that capacitive reactance decreases with increasing frequency while inductive reactance increases with frequency. When an alternating current is applied to a resistance, the alternating voltage across the resistance is *in phase* with the current. The voltage across a capacitance *lags* the current by 90°. The voltage across an inductance *leads* the current by 90°.

If resistance and reactance are in series, the impedance is not the simple sum of these quantities. Instead, at any given frequency:

$$Z = \sqrt{(R^2 + X^2)}$$

The phase angle between applied and resultant voltage is given by:

$$\tan \varphi = X/R$$

Similar relationships apply to quantities which are the inverse of the above. The admittance (Y) of a circuit, expressed in siemens (or mhos) may consist of two parts, conductance G and susceptance (B), also expressed in siemens. Susceptance may consist of two parts, capacitive susceptance (B_C) and inductive susceptance (B_L). Conductance is independent of frequency but both types of susceptance are dependent on frequency:

$$B_C = 2\pi f C \qquad B_L = \frac{1}{2\pi f L}$$

When an alternating voltage is applied to a conductance, the alternating current across the conductance is *in phase* with the voltage. The current through a capacitance *leads* the voltage by 90°. The current through an inductance *lags* the voltage by 90°.

146

If conductance and susceptance are in parallel, the admittance is not the simple sum of these quantities. Instead, at any given frequency:

$$Y = \sqrt{(G^2 + B^2)}$$

The phase angle between applied and resultant current is given by:

$$\tan \varphi = B/G$$

Impedance matching is often essential when joining two circuits together. The aim is to ensure that the maximum voltage signal is transferred from the output of one circuit to the input of the other. If the output impedance (Z_{OUT}) of the first circuit is equal to or slightly less than the input impedance (Z_{IN}) of the second circuit, there is no problem. However, impedance matching often involves matching a high Z_{OUT} to a low Z_{IN}. Failure to do this generally leads to a partial or almost total loss of signal. Several techniques are available:

(1) Bipolar transistor in the common-collector (voltage follower) configuration; see p.98.
(2) JFET in the common-drain configuration; see p.102.
(3) Operational amplifier wired as a unity gain voltage follower; see p.108.
(4) Transformer, as explained in the next section.

Impedance matching by transformer
Use is made of the fact that if the load on the secondary coil of a transformer is R_L, the *apparent* input resistance of the primary coil R_{IN} is:

$$R_{IN} = R_L/n^2$$

where n is the turns ratio, the number of secondary turns (N_2) divided by the number of primary turns (N_1). A more useful form of this equation is:

$$n = \sqrt{(R_L/R_{IN})}$$

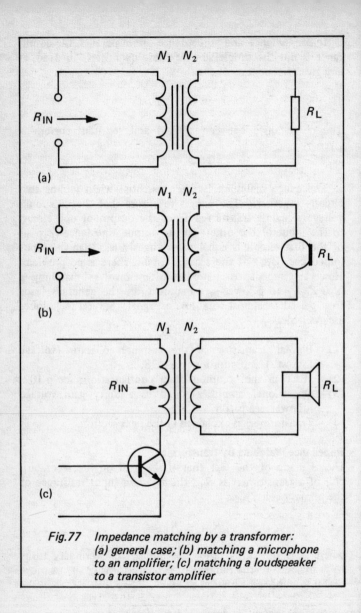

*Fig.77   Impedance matching by a transformer:
(a) general case; (b) matching a microphone
to an amplifier; (c) matching a loudspeaker
to a transistor amplifier*

For a step-up transformer $n > 1$: for a step-down transformer $n < 1$. The general case is illustrated in Figure 77(a), where we can say that R_{IN} is the input resistance of the load as seen by a device connected to the input terminals. For example, a step-up transformer has a turns ratio 9 (i.e. N_2/N_1 = 9). Its secondary coil is connected to a load resistance R_L of 10kΩ. The input resistance, $R_{IN} = 10kΩ/9^2 = 10kΩ/81$ = 123Ω. The same considerations also apply to impedance in general.

A common use for this technique is to use a step-down transformer to match a low-impedance microphone to a high-impedance amplifier (Fig.77(b)). Example: a microphone has an output impedance of 200Ω and is to be connected to an amplifier with input impedance of 10kΩ. $R_L = 200Ω$ and the amplifier is to see this as a resistance of 10kΩ. The required turns ratio is:

$$n = \sqrt{(200/10000)} = \sqrt{0.02} = 0.14$$

$1/0.14 = 7$, so we use a step-down transformer with a 1:7 turns ratio. The amplifier then sees the microphone as having an impedance of 10kΩ.

Transformers are sometimes used for matching a loudspeaker (low impedance) to the relatively high-impedance output of an amplifier (Fig.77(c)). Example: an 8Ω loudspeaker is to be matched to a transistor amplifier circuit in which an impedance of 250Ω is suited to its operating conditions (i.e. the transistor would be operating correctly if there was a 250Ω resistor in its collector circuit instead of the transformer coil). Connecting an 8Ω speaker directly into the collector circuit would give very low volume as only a small portion of the power would be developed in the speaker. If we use a transformer:

$$n = \sqrt{(8/250)} = \sqrt{0.032} = 0.18$$

$1/0.18 = 6$ (approx.) so we need a step-down transformer with 1:6 turns ratio. The transistor then sees the speaker as a 250Ω resistor.

This technique is also used in radio frequency circuits where one of the windings of the transformer may be part of a tuned circuit, functioning as a band-pass filter.

17 Oscillators

1 Hartley oscillator

This oscillator (Fig.78) produces a sine wave output. The resonant circuit L1, C produces oscillations with frequency

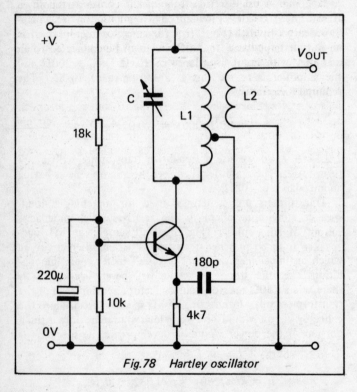

Fig.78   Hartley oscillator

$1/2\pi\sqrt{LC}$. The oscillator is tuned by varying C: this can be replaced by a fixed capacitor if preferred. The coil consists of a number of turns (p.29) wound on a ferrite rod, and tapped at the centre turn. For audio applications, a 1.5mH coil can be made by winding 350 turns of 32swg enamelled wire on a 10mm diameter ferrite rod, 75mm long. The coil is tapped toward one end to provide feedback to the emitter of the transistor. Output is taken from a coil of a few turns (L2) wound on the same former. Ready-made inductors are also available. The transistor can be any high-gain low-power type, such as the BC109, provided that it has sufficient bandwidth for the frequency range required. Resistor values given in the figure are suitable for a 6V supply; resistors for other supply voltages can be calculated as for a common collector amplifier (p.98). The Hartley oscillator is seldom used at audio frequencies because of the size of the inductor required. It is much more popular as a radio-frequency generator, in which case an r.f. transistor is appropriate.

2 Colpitts oscillator

This is another sine wave oscillator (Fig.79) but the feedback is taken from the capacitive side of the resonant circuit instead of from the inductive side. In calculating the frequency, use the combined series capacitance of the two capacitors. In other respects the remarks made about the Hartley oscillator apply also to this circuit.

3 Phase shift oscillator

This is more useful than the above for producing sine waves at audio frequency. The frequency of the oscillator is determined by the phase shift network consisting of 3 resistors and 3 capacitors (Fig.80), and is given by:

$$f = 1/2\pi \sqrt{(6RC)}$$

In theory the 3 resistors of the phase shift network are equal in value. The base resistor R_B must also be taken into account, so the value of the third resistor R^* is calculated from:

$$R^* = \frac{R \times R_B}{R_B - R}$$

This gives R^* a value such that R^* and R_B in parallel are equal

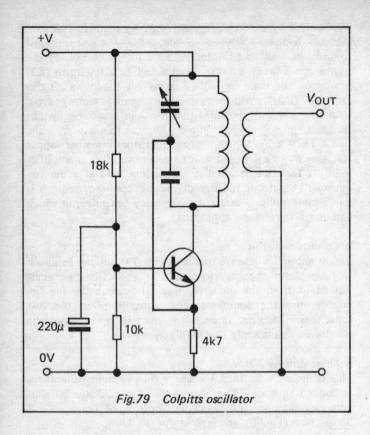

+V

V_{OUT}

18k

220μ

10k

4k7

0V

Fig.79   Colpitts oscillator

to R. A Darlington transistor such as the MPSA14 (p.35) can be used instead of the 2 separate transistors shown in the figure. This is a simple circuit which is best used as a fixed-frequency oscillator. It is not practicable to tune it by altering the resistors, as this entails altering R_B as well. If it must be tunable, use a triple ganged capacitor — not an easy component to find!

4 Wien bridge oscillator
This produces low-distortion sine waves at audio frequencies. The frequency depends upon the phase shift network of 2 resistors and 2 capacitors (Fig.81):

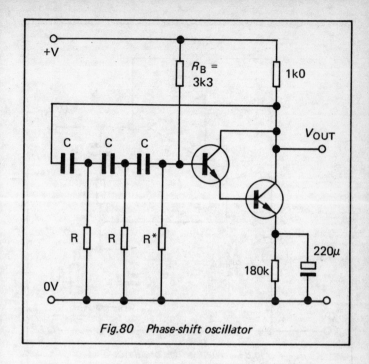

Fig.80 Phase-shift oscillator

$$f = 1/2\pi RC$$

For stable operation the gain of the amplifier has to be maintained at exactly 3. The filament lamp provides variable negative feedback with a long time constant. The variable resistor is adjusted so that the overall feedback level is just sufficient to keep the oscillator running yet without saturating. The oscillator has high output impedance so its signal should be passed to a voltage follower or an amplifier with very high input impedance.

18 Function generators

1 UJT oscillators

One of the simplest sawtooth generators is the unijunction oscillator (Fig.82(a)). The two outputs of this provide a

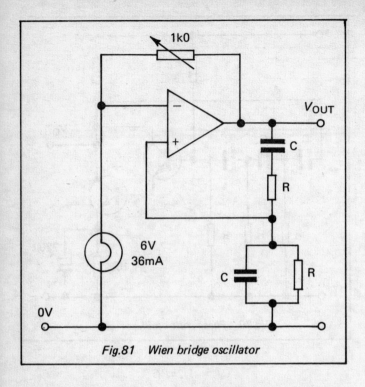

Fig.81   Wien bridge oscillator

sawtooth waveform and a series of trigger pulses, respectively.
The wave ramps up from about 2V (the valley point, V_V) to
the peak point (V_P). The peak point depends on the supply
voltage V_S and the stand-off ratio of the transistor. The
stand-off ratio varies from about 0.56 to 0.75 in different
transistors, 0.6 being a typical value. The time of one
oscillation is approximately:

$$t = -RC \times \ln[(1 - \eta)/(1 - V_V/V_S)]$$

where 'ln' indicates the use of natural logarithms. Taking
typical values, $V_S = 6$, $V_V = 2$, and $\eta = 0.6$, this reduces to:

$$t = -RC \times (\ln[0.4/(1 - 0.333)]) = -RC \times \ln[0.6]$$

154

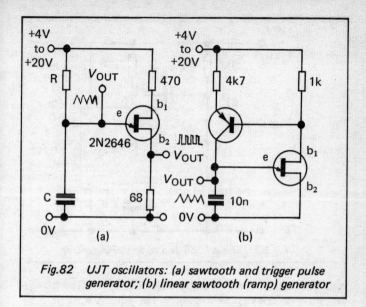

Fig.82   UJT oscillators: (a) sawtooth and trigger pulse generator; (b) linear sawtooth (ramp) generator

$$= -RC \times (-0.51)$$

Thus $t \approx 0.5RC$

For example, if $C = 1\mu F$, $R = 10k\Omega$, then $t = 0.005$, and $f = 1/t = 200Hz$.

Since the charging of the capacitor is exponential, the rising slope of the sawtooth is not linear. This makes little difference for most audio applications. Figure 82(b) shows the capacitor being charged through a constant-current circuit. This makes the rising slope linear. The rate of charge of the capacitor is now constant, independent of V_S, though V_S still affects the peak point. Since the current depends upon the gain of the transistor, there is no easy formula for calculating frequency. Run at low frequencies, this circuit has applications as a ramp generator.

2 NE566 function generator

The NE566 (Fig.83) produces a symmetrical triangular wave

155

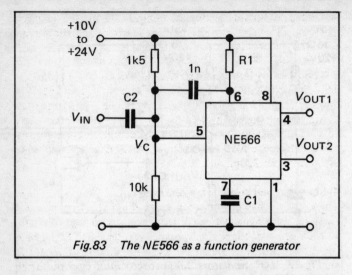

Fig.83   The NE566 as a function generator

and a square wave with exactly 50% duty cycle. The triangular wave is 2.4V peak-to-peak. The square wave is 5.4V peak-to-peak, with a rise time of 20ns and a fall time of 50ns. Frequency is determined by the value of R1 and C1, and of the control voltage V_C. V_C can be set to any value in the range from 3/4 of the supply voltage V^+ to the full supply voltage. R1 must be in the range 2kΩ to 20kΩ. The maximum frequency is 1MHz. The formula for calculating frequency is:

$$f = \frac{2(V^+ - V_C)}{R1 \times C1 \times V^+}$$

For example, with the biasing resistors as shown in the figure and V^+ = 12V, then V_C = 12 × 10/11.5 = 10.43V (see p.77). If R1 = 10kΩ and C1 = 10nF, then:

$$f = 2(12 - 10.43)/(10 \times 10^3 \times 10 \times 10^{-9} \times 12) = 2.6\text{kHz}$$

An alternating signal at V_{IN} modulates V_C and varies the frequency. In this way frequency can be swept over a 10:1 range. Capacitor C2 can be omitted and a fixed frequency generated by suitably setting the values of the biasing resistors. The control voltage can also be supplied from another circuit, provided that it stays in the specified range.

3 Triangle wave and square wave generator

This circuit (Fig.84) is based on two op amps. Two JFET op amps in the LF353 package are very suitable. The frequency of the output signals is given by $f = 1/RC$. The circuit has a very wide operating range without distortion. R can have any value between 330Ω and about $4.7M\Omega$; C takes any value between about 220pF and $2\mu F$.

4 Sine wave and cosine wave generator

This circuit is based on two op amps (Fig.85). They produce two sine wave signals of equal frequency but $90°$ out of phase, so the output of the second op amp is referred to as a cosine wave. Frequency is varied by selecting suitable values for R and C. R is in the range $220k\Omega$ to $10M\Omega$; C is in the range 39pF to 22nF. The relationship between R, C and f is complicated, as the values of other resistors and capacitors have to be taken into account. As a starting point, make $R = 220k\Omega$ and $C = 18nF$, which gives a frequency of 250Hz. The Zener diodes are 3.9V or 4.7V diodes of low power rating.

5 The 8038 function generator

This versatile ic produces square waves, triangle waves and very accurate sine waves (Fig.86), with a very wide frequency range. The two variable resistors shown are used when adjusting the sine wave output; an oscilloscope is required to observe the wave shape. However, if an oscilloscope is not available, connect pins 1 and 12 as shown in Figure 87, to obtain an output that is reasonably close to a sine wave.

The duty cycle can be varied. With the $2.2k\Omega$ resistors connected to pins 4 and 5 as shown, the duty cycle is 50%. If these are replaced with other resistors, for example with $5k\Omega$ connected to pin 4 and 820 connected to pin 5, the waveform becomes asymmetrical. The square wave becomes a pulsed wave, with long pulses separated by intervals about one-sixteenth of a pulse. This is useful in musical circuits since the pulse wave is richer in even harmonics than the

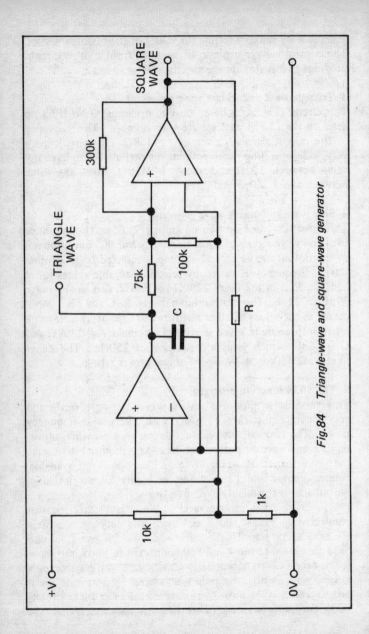

Fig.84   Triangle-wave and square-wave generator

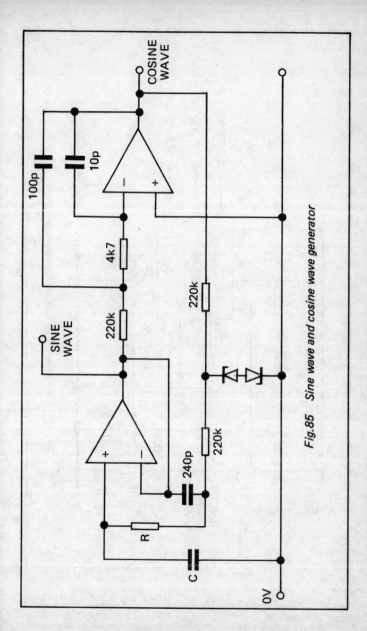

Fig.85   Sine wave and cosine wave generator

159

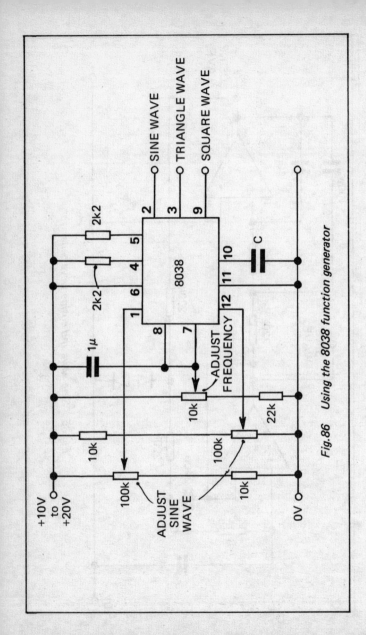

Fig.86 Using the 8038 function generator

160

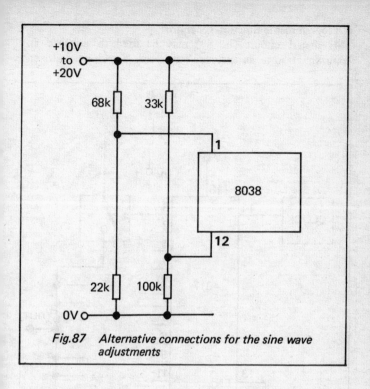

Fig.87   Alternative connections for the sine wave adjustments

square wave.   The triangle wave becomes a sawtooth wave, also very rich in harmonics and useful in musical applications. The sine wave too is modified, though there are no clear applications for this.

The basic frequency is set by capacitor *C*, for example, by switching in different capacitors of suitable values, and the ic can be made to span the range 0.001Hz to 1MHz in 40:1 sweeps.   100nF is a suitable capacitor value for most audio applications.   Frequency is swept over each range by varying the control voltage applied to pin 7.

One of the outputs is selected by switching and fed to a 100kΩ variable resistor, the other end of which is taken to the positive supply.   The signal is obtained from the wiper of the resistor and varies in amplitude according to the setting.

161

6 Programmable function generator

This digital circuit (Fig.88) may be used to produce an approximation to an analogue waveform. The circuit is driven

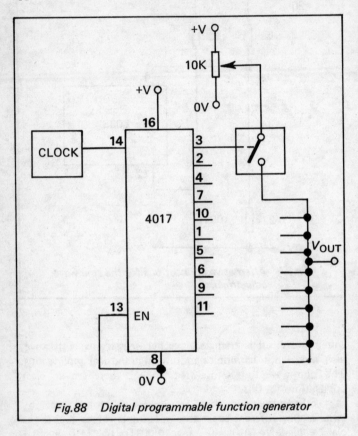

Fig.88   Digital programmable function generator

by a clock, which may be almost any kind of astable circuit, such as the 555 astable described on p.225. The clock frequency is 10 times the frequency of the required function. The clock causes the 10 outputs of the 4017 counter to go high in turn.. As each output goes high, it turns on (i.e. closes) one of 10 analogue switches. For simplicity, only one of these is shown in the figure. The switches can be provided by three

4016 or 4066 quadruple analogue switch ic's or by other analogue switches listed on p.196.

One side of each switch is connected to a potential divider consisting of a 10kΩ variable resistor. This can be set to any voltage between 0V and the supply. At any instant just *one* of the switches is on and the voltage provided by its potential divider appears as V_{OUT}. As the circuit runs, the 10 preset voltages appear as a programmed waveform at V_{OUT}.

As an example of programming a waveform, consider a sine wave with frequency 250Hz, 2V peak-to-peak, centred on 3V. The clock is set to run at 2500Hz. Figure 89 shows the voltages required at 10 equal intervals of time (0.4ms). Construct a table like this:

Time	θ	$\theta + 18$	$sin(\theta + 18)$	$3 + sin(\theta + 18)$
0	0	18	0.31	3.31
0.4	36	54	0.81	3.81
0.8	72	90	1.00	4.00
1.2	108	126	0.81	3.81
1.6	144	162	0.31	3.31

and so on to . . .

| 3.6 | 324 | 342 | −0.31 | 2.69 |

In this example we have divided the phase angle into 10 equal steps of 36°. However, if we start from zero, we by-pass the 90° step at which $sin \theta = 1$ and thus the wave does not have its full amplitude. This is why 18° is added to all stages before taking the sines. The figures in the final column are the voltages to which the potential dividers should be set.

The output is stepped, so it is by no means as smooth as a true sine wave. This gives rise to high-frequency harmonics in the signal. The output can be smoothed to a certain extent by connecting a capacitor (say 10µF) between V_{OUT} and the 0V rail. If the capacitance is right the smoothed output *just* reaches the current value of V_{OUT} as the output steps to its next value.

Other more complex waveforms may be programmed in the same way but there is a limit to what can be done with only 10 voltage steps. Using a longer counter with say 20 or 30 steps would give a better result, but the circuit is considerably

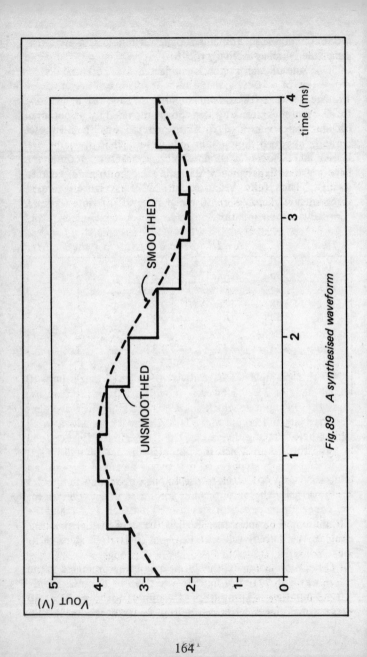

Fig.89   A synthesised waveform

164

more complicated. For complex waveforms it is best to use signals derived from other types of function generator, mixing them in the required proportions.

19 Thyristor and triac circuits

In all circuits which are mains-powered, check that all components used are rated to withstand the high voltage and currents to which they will be subjected. When designing the layout, check safety aspects with extreme care. Unless you have previous experience of designing and constructing mains circuits, check fully with someone who has already undertaken such work successfully.

Figure 90 is a basic half-wave power controller. The thyristor is rated at 400V PIV and for a current of 4A; a

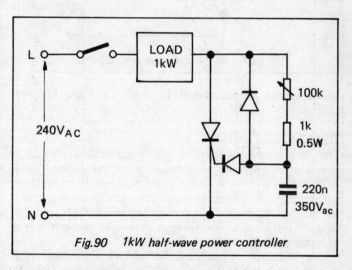

Fig.90   1kW half-wave power controller

C106D would be suitable, though a thyristor of higher rating could be used to give an extra margin of safety. The diodes are also rated at 400V PIV; 1N4004 is suggested. Other ratings appear in the figure. A heat sink may be needed for the thyristor (p.72).

The full-wave lamp dimmer of Figure 91 is a more efficient power control circuit, though limited to 100W. As above, the

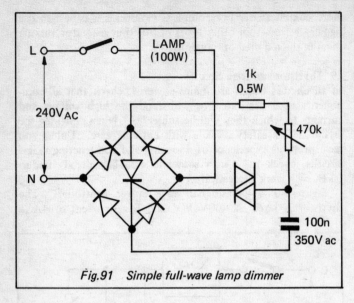

Fig.91   Simple full-wave lamp dimmer

thyristor and diodes should be rated to 400V PIV, or more.

RFI filter

One of the snags of thyristor and triac circuits is that they generate radio-frequency interference on the mains. This may be removed or at least reduced to tolerable amounts by interposing a RFI filter between the control circuit and the mains. Such filters can be purchased ready-made and are often constructed as lead-through devices to be mounted on an earthed chassis.

An RFI filter circuit is shown in Figure 92, employing two radio-frequency chokes and 3 capacitors rated to withstand mains voltage. The usual safety precautions should be taken when building this filter.

20   Motor control circuits

The circuits described in this section are intended only for the control of low-voltage d.c. motors, such as might be used in working models or small robots.

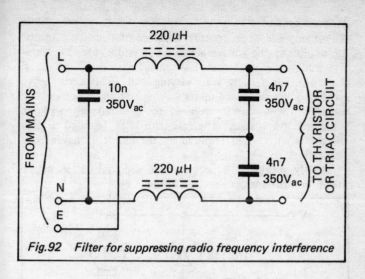

Fig.92   Filter for suppressing radio frequency interference

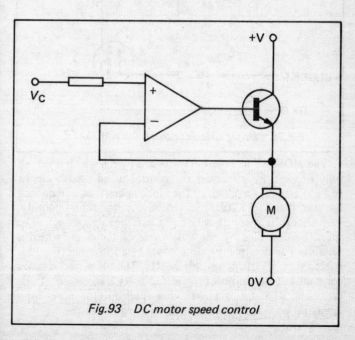

Fig.93   DC motor speed control

1 Speed control

An op amp is used to control the speed of a small d.c. motor by monitoring the voltage across its armature (Fig.93). Negative feedback ensures that this remains constant even though back e.m.f. is varying with varying load. This circuit gives greater stability of speed under varying load and is particularly useful if the motor is required to run smoothly without stalling at low speeds. The transistor must be rated to pass the maximum current required by the motor; it may need a heat sink.

Strictly speaking, the next circuit is digital but its *effect* puts it into the analogue section of the book.

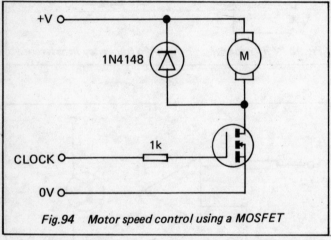

Fig.94   Motor speed control using a MOSFET

The MOSFET in Figure 94 acts as a switch which is turned fully on or fully off under the control of an astable circuit (p.215) acting as a 'clock'. The clock operates at a frequency (greater than, say, 20Hz) so that the motor runs smoothly, even though it is continually being switched on and off. The speed is controlled by the duty cycle of the clock, which is variable. For example the clock could be a 555 timer (Fig.131, p.225) with a variable resistor as R1. The off-period remains constant but the on-time is increased as R1 is increased. Thus, increasing R1 results in power being applied to the motor for a longer proportion of the time and its speed increases.

2 Direction control

A relay is often used to control the direction of a d.c. motor. The relay has dual change-over contacts, connected as in Figure 95(a). The relay coil is activated by direct switching

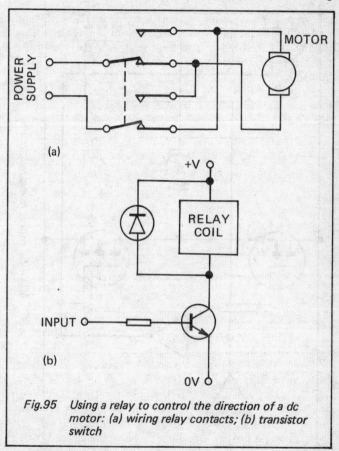

(a)

(b)

Fig.95 Using a relay to control the direction of a dc motor: (a) wiring relay contacts; (b) transistor switch

or, especially if the relay is to be under the control of a logic circuit, by a switching transistor (Fig.95(b)). Component values are calculated as for a common-emitter amplifier (p.92). Add the protective diode if the relay does not include one already.

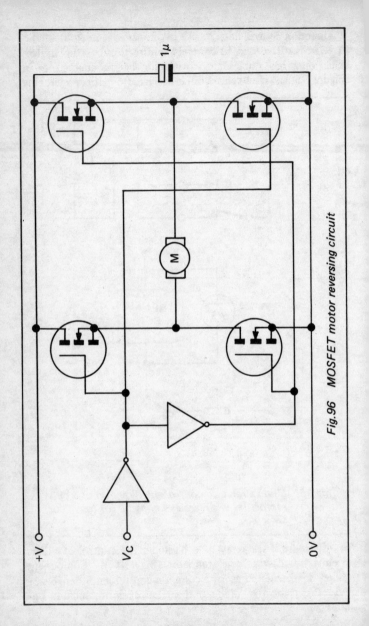

Fig.96 MOSFET motor reversing circuit

170

Figure 96 shows how to use two inverters and four MOS-FETs to achieve the same effect as the relay circuit above. Select MOSFETs rated to withstand the maximum motor current. This circuit can be used in conjunction with the speed control circuit of section 1 above.

Chapter 4

DIGITAL CIRCUITS

1 Choosing a logic family
The main logic families are:

TTL:
    74 Series, original widely-used TTL series, less popular now.
    74LS Series, low-power Schottky.
    74ALS Series, fast low-power Schottky.

CMOS:
    4000 Series, the original CMOS series, still very popular.

CMOS versions of TTL:
    74HC Series
    74HCT Series, input levels TTL compatible.
    74AC Series, faster.
    74ACT Series, faster, input TTL compatible.

Table 7 overleaf lists the advantageous features of each family and is intended to help you choose which family or families to use for a given project. For more critical aspects, check the parameters, Tables 7, 8 and 9, or the manufacturers' data sheets.

The 74HC and 74HCT series are to be preferred for almost all applications. CMOS logic has the disadvantage that special handling precautions must be taken to prevent damage to the input by static charges. The original 'A' series has been replaced by the improved 'B' series, as indicated by the suffix on type numbers. Within the CMOS family, some ic's are available with *unbuffered outputs*, indicated by a 'U' in the device number, e.g. 4001BE and 4001UBE. Unbuffered inputs are preferable for analogue applications. UBE logic has shorter propagation delay times.

See p.187 for details of fanout.

2 Logic gates
Table 8 is an index to simple gate functions, listing the corresponding ic's in the 74 series and the CMOS 4000 series. Most

Table 7 – LOGIC FAMILIES

Feature	TTL			4000	CMOS			
	74	74LS	74ALS		74HC	74HCT	74AC	74ACT
Wide operating voltage range				*	*		*	
Power (L = low, LL = very low)		L	L	LL	LL	LL	LL	LL
TTL compatibility	*	*	*			*		*
Speed (F = fast, FF = very fast)	F	F	FF		F	F	FF	FF
Range of logic devices available (* = wide, ** = complete)	*	**	*	**	*	**		
Parameter								
Operating voltage (must be regulated if a single figure is quoted)†	5	5	5	3–15	2–6	5	2–6	5
Typical propagation delay time (ns)†	10	10	5	105	10	10	5	3
Max. clock frequency (MHz)	35	40	–	12	40	–	100	–

† in CMOS, propagation delay is greater when supply voltage is at the low end of the range; if this is important, operate at high end of range.

Table 8 – SIMPLE GATE FUNCTIONS

TRUE (non-inverting) and NOT (inverting) gates

TRUE	NOT (INVERT)	
7407*+	7404	4049+
4050+	7405*	4069
4106^S	7406**	40106^S
4584^S	7414^S	4502^Y
	7416*	

*   open collector outputs

**   high voltage open collector outputs

\+   buffers

^{S} Schmitt trigger inputs

^{Y} with strobe

---

of those listed for the 74 series are available in the 74LS and 74HC series, and possibly the other 74 series; many are no longer available in the standard 74 series.

Three useful gate ic's which do not fit into the tables are:

(1)   4000 – triple 3-input NOR *plus* inverter (NOT)
(2)   4007 – dual complementary pair *plus* interverter (p.181)
(3)   4530 – dual 5-input majority logic gate.

Table 8 does not include devices such as quad or octal buffers with 3-state outputs, which have the main function of communicating with data buses rather than performing logical operations. All gates have 1 input, with 6 gates per package. The 4049 is available with buffered (4049B) and unbuffered (4049UB) outputs. The 4069 is available only as the 4069UB.

The number in brackets in the first column of Table 9 is the number of gates per package. Where one particular series is listed, the device is available only in that series. The 4001, 4002, 4011, 4012, 4023, and 4025 are available with either buffered ('B') or unbuffered ('UB') outputs.

Table 9 – OTHER LOGIC GATES

No. of inputs	AND	NAND	OR	NOR	Logical function Ex-OR	Ex-NOR
2 (4)	7408 7409* 4081	7400 7401* 7403* 7426** 7437+ 7438*+ 74132S 4011 4093S	7432 4071	7402 7428+ 7433*+ 74128 4001	7486 74LS136* 74LS386 4070	4077 74LS266*
3 (3)	7411 7415* 4073	7410 7412* 4023 7413S	4075	7427 4025		
4 (2)	7421 4082	7420 7422* 7440+ 4012	4072	7425Y 4002		
5 (2)				74LS260		
8 (1)		7430 4068		4078 4080		
13 (1)		74133				

For meanings of indexes, see the list at the end of Table 8.

176

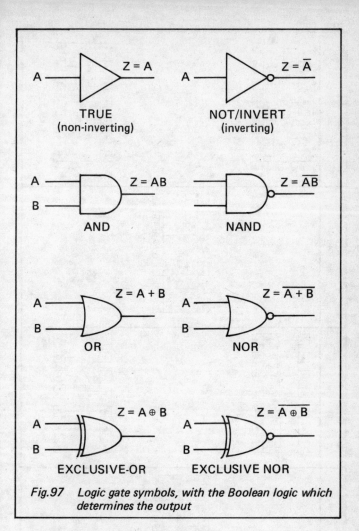

Fig.97   Logic gate symbols, with the Boolean logic which determines the output

Figure 97 gives the symbols for logic gates according to the American standard (MIL/ANSI) which is widely used both in the US and in Britain. AND, NAND, OR and NOR gates may have more than 2 inputs. Figure 98 shows the pinouts.

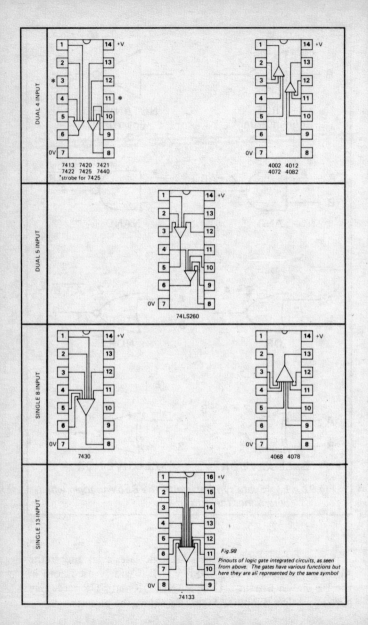

Fig.98
Pinouts of logic gate integrated circuits, as seen from above. The gates have various functions but here they are all represented by the same symbol

178

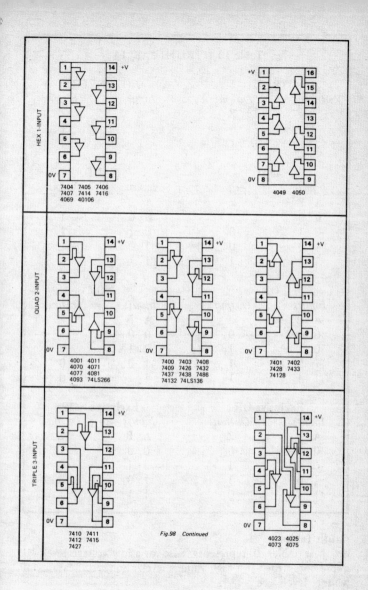

HEX 1-INPUT

7404 7405 7406
7407 7414 7416
4069 40106

4049 4050

QUAD 2-INPUT

4001 4011
4070 4071
4077 4081
4093 74LS266

7400 7403 7408
7409 7426 7432
7437 7438 7486
74132 74LS136

7401 7402
7428 7433
74128

TRIPLE 3-INPUT

7410 7411
7412 7415
7427

Fig.98 Continued

4023 4025
4073 4075

179

Table 10 – TRUTH TABLES

TRUE			NOT/INVERT	
Input	*Output*		*Input*	*Output*
A	Z		A	Z
0	0		0	1
1	1		1	0

AND			NAND	
Inputs	*Output*		*Inputs*	*Output*
A B	Z		A B	Z
0 0	0		0 0	1
0 1	0		0 1	1
1 0	0		1 0	1
1 1	1		1 1	0

OR			NOR	
Inputs	*Output*		*Inputs*	*Output*
A B	Z		A B	Z
0 0	0		0 0	1
0 1	1		0 1	0
1 0	1		1 0	0
1 1	1		1 1	0

Exclusive-OR			Exclusive-NOR	
Inputs	*Output*		*Inputs*	*Output*
A B	Z		A B	Z
0 0	0		0 0	1
0 1	1		0 1	0
1 0	1		1 0	0
1 1	0		1 1	1

Truth Tables

In these tables '0' represents 'false' or a low voltage level; '1' represents 'true' or a high voltage level. For specifications of voltage levels, see p.189.

By extension, truth tables of gates with more than 2 inputs may be derived from the tables for AND, NAND, OR and

NOR. For example the output of a 4-input NAND gate is low if and only if *all* its inputs are high.

Logical equivalents

Often a circuit requires only one or two of a certain type of gate yet there are spare gates of other types. It saves expense, power and board space to use the spare gates to perform the function of the missing gate. Figure 99 shows some ways of using spare gates. Where the figure shows NAND or NOR gates with inputs wired together, gates with 3 or more inputs can also be used. In circuits in which timing is important the additional delay resulting from the use of multiple gates may cause problems, but this is unlikely to happen.

Often only one Ex-OR gate is needed, yet these gates are relatively expensive. Figure 100 shows three ways of obtaining the Ex-OR function using other gates. In Figure 100(a) and 100(b), the NOT gates can be NAND or NOR gates with their inputs wired together, as in Figure 99(c). Figure 100(c) uses four NAND gates, possibly using a single 7400 or 4011 ic. Circuits such as these may also be useful if other functions of A and B are required in addition to the Ex-OR function.

With the 74 series, the OR function can be obtained by using gates with open-collector outputs. The outputs are wired together and a pull-up resistor is used, as in Figure 101(a). This technique may also be used with open-collector NOR, AND or NAND outputs to give a variety of logical functions. Figure 101(b) shows an example, $Z = (A \text{ AND } B)$ OR $(C \text{ AND } D)$.

The 4007 integrated circuit

Although this is a whole ic, it is a cheap one and may be used to construct a wide variety of logic gates. It consists of two complementary pairs of n-channel and p-channel MOSFETs, each of which is individually accessible, and a third pair of complementary MOSFETs connected as an inverter (Fig. 102(a)). As well as the possibility of using the MOSFETs in many different ways for switching or amplifying, there are several ways of connecting these building blocks to make up a number of types of logic gate. The remainder of Figure 102 shows the connections. The 4007 has unbuffered outputs but

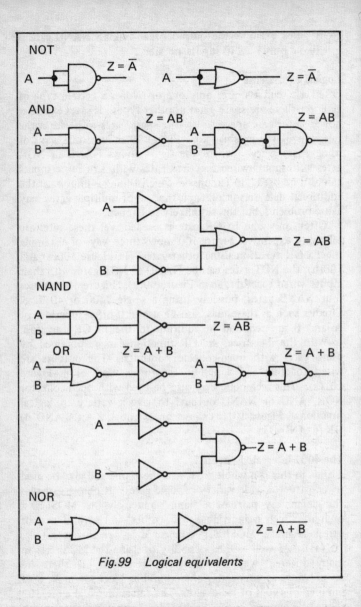

Fig.99 Logical equivalents

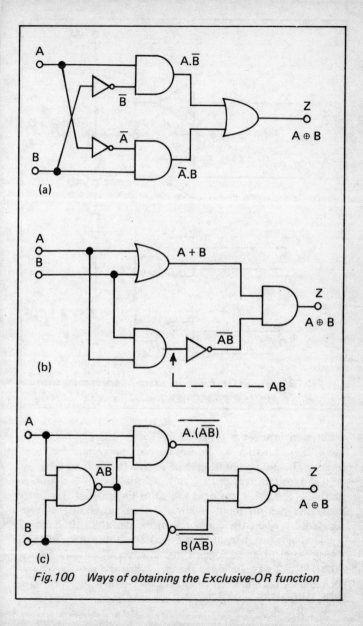

Fig.100 Ways of obtaining the Exclusive-OR function

183

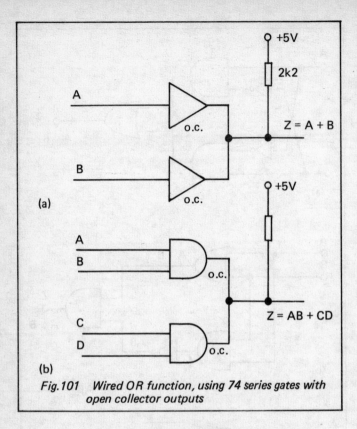

(a)

$Z = A + B$

(b)

$Z = AB + CD$

Fig.101   Wired OR function, using 74 series gates with open collector outputs

a buffered inverter is provided by Figure 102(c). It has the same characteristics as an inverter of the regular buffered series. The 3-input NOR gate of Figure 102(f) is very handy as it may often happen that only a single gate of this kind is needed. The single analogue switch of Figure 102(h) is open when the control input is low. It then has almost infinite resistance. When the control is made high the switch closes and has a resistance of about 600Ω. It provides for the transmission of an analogue signal in either direction. Figure 102(i) is a 2-way analogue switch. When the control is low, INA/OUTA is connected to OUTC/INC. When the control is high, INB/OUTB and OUTC/INC are connected.

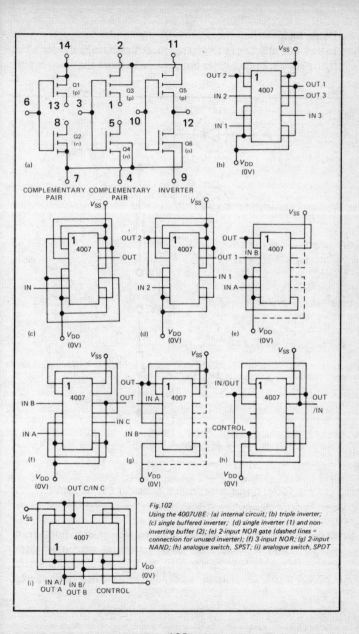

Fig.102
Using the 4007UBE: (a) internal circuit; (b) triple inverter;
(c) single buffered inverter; (d) single inverter (1) and non-
inverting buffer (2); (e) 2-input NOR gate (dashed lines =
connection for unused inverter); (f) 3-input NOR; (g) 2-input
NAND; (h) analogue switch, SPST; (i) analogue switch, SPDT

185

Diode logic

Figure 103 illustrates two gates constructed using diodes. The figure shows 2-input gates but gates with more than two inputs

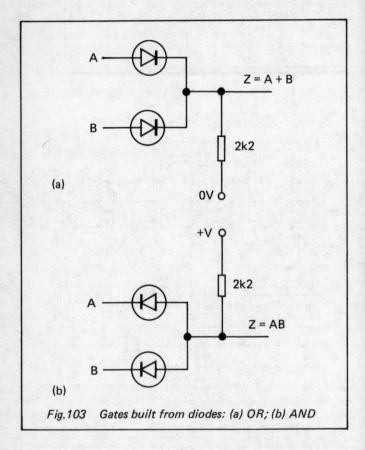

Fig.103   Gates built from diodes: (a) OR; (b) AND

may be built up on the same principle. Gates built from diodes will not necessarily work as well as regular ic gates, especially in fast-acting circuits, so it is well to check the operation of the circuit carefully when using such gates.

3 Fanout and interfacing

Fanout between the main logic families

The table below shows the maximum number of gates that can be driven from an output of a given family. Certain buffer devices have special outputs intended for driving more gates.

Table 11 – MAXIMUM NUMBER OF GATES

| Driving output | Driven input | | |
| | | TTL | CMOS |
	74	74LS/ALS	all families
TTL 74	10	20	*
TTL 74 buffers	30	60	*
TTL 74LS/ALS	5	20	*
TTL 74LS buffers	15	60	*
CMOS 4000	+	1	50
CMOS 74HC/HCT	2	10	*
CMOS 74HC/HCT buffers	4	15	*
CMOS 74AC/ACT	15	60	*

* in practice, the number is unlimited.   + not possible.

Fanout to other devices

It is essential that, when an output is connected to a number of other logic inputs, the current drawn by these inputs should not significantly alter the voltage level at the output gate. This condition must be met at both low and high logic levels. The fanout table above reflects this for interfaces between members of the same or other logic families. On occasions it is necessary to interface between a logic family and a device of another kind, such as a microprocessor. If only a few inputs are involved, the table above gives sufficiently good guidance. In particular, any output can usually drive many CMOS inputs.

At low level (logic 0) the output must be able to drain enough current from all the inputs to which it is connected, so as to pull them down to a logic low level. In other words, the minimum output current (I_{OL}) of a device must be numerically equal to or greater than the total of the maximum input currents (ΣI_{IL}) of the devices to which it is fanned out. we use the phrase 'numerically equal to' because I_{OH} flows toward a current drain so it is quoted as a *negative*, while I_{IH} flows from a current source and so is quoted as a *positive* current. Table 12 lists values of the currents used calculating fanout at logic low level. For buffers, see p.271.

Table 12

Parameter	74	74LS	74HC/HCT	74AC	4000
I_{OL} (min)	16mA	8mA	4mA (@4.5V)	4mA (@3V)	0.44mA (@5V)
				24mA (@4.5V)	1.1mA (@10V)
				24mA (@5.5V)	3mA (@15V)
I_{IL} (max)	−1.6mA	−0.4mA	−0.1µA (@6V)	−0.1µA (@5.5V)	−0.3µA (@15V)

This table shows, for example, that a 74 output (16mA) can be fanned out to forty 74LS inputs (40 × 0.4mA = 16mA) and that one 74HC output (4mA) can be fanned out to ten 74LS inputs (10 × 0.4mA = 4mA). These fanouts apply at low level, but we must check to see if they apply at high level too.

At high level (logic 1) the output must be able to supply enough current to all the inputs it is connected to, so as to pull them up to a logic high level. In other words, the minimum output current (I_{OH}) of a device must be numerically equal to or greater than the total of the maximum input currents (ΣI_{IH}) of the devices to which it is fanned out.

Table 13 lists values of the currents used calculating fanout at logic high level:

Parameter	74	74LS	74HC/HCT	74AC	4000
I_{OH} (min)	−0.4mA	−0.4mA	−4mA	−4mA (@3V)	−0.16mA (@5V)
				−24mA (@4.5V)	−0.4mA (@10V)
				−24mA (@5.5V)	−1.2mA (@15V)
I_{IH} (max)	40µA	20µA	0.1µA	0.1µA (@5.5V)	0.3µA (@15V)

Table 13

This table shows, for example, that a 74 output (0.4mA) can be fanned out to twenty 74LS inputs (20 × 20µA = 0.4 mA) and that one 74HC output (4mA) can be fanned out to ten 74LS inputs (10 × 0.4mA = 4mA).

As an example of fanning out to other kinds of device, the output of the ZN427E A-to-D converter (p.255) has I_{OL} = 1.6mA, so it can be fanned out to one standard 74 input, four 74LS outputs (4 × 0.4mA = 1.6mA, see previous table). At high level I_{OH} = −100µA, so it could be fanned out to two 74 inputs (2 × 40µA = 80µA) or five 74LS outputs (2 × 20µA = 100µA) but we have just shown that the low-level currents limit the fanout to one 74 or four 74LS inputs. It can fan out to a large number of CMOS inputs at both levels.

Interfacing the main logic families

Figure 104 shows input and output thresholds for the main logic families. It also shows the operating voltage ranges. For 74, 74LS, 74HCT and 74ACT the thresholds are indicated by symbols at the standard supply voltage, 5V. For 4000, 74HC and 74AC the thresholds vary with supply voltage and are shown as straight lines. This chart can also be used

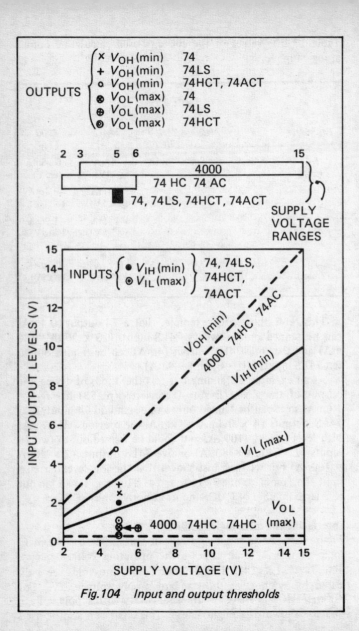

Fig. 104   Input and output thresholds

when interfacing logic with analogue circuits.

For a logic output to reliably send a meaningful signal to the input of another type of logic family the following conditions must apply:

(a) the minimum logic high output (V_{OH}) must be higher than the minimum logic high input (V_{IH});

(b) the maximum logic low output (V_{OL}) must be lower than the maximum logic low input (V_{IL}).

This can be clearly seen by examining the lines for the 4000, 74HC and 74AC series. The minimum V_{OH} is within 0.5V of the supply voltage, while the maximum voltage required to count as a high input (V_{IH}) is two-thirds of the supply voltage. There is a margin of almost one-third of the supply voltage to allow for noise. Similarly, the maximum V_{OL} is within 0.5V of the ground line while the minimum voltage that counts as a low input is one-third of supply. The same features are found with the voltages for the 74, 74LS, 74HCT and 74ACT series.

Provided that these two conditions above apply, and taking fanout requirements into account, devices of different series may be freely interfaced. The only exceptions, as can be seen from the Figure 104 are when TTL outputs (74, 74LS) are fed to CMOS inputs (4000, 74HC, 74AC). At 5V the minimum high outputs (symbols + and x) are less than the minimum high inputs. Consequently a pull-up resistor is needed at each output. When interfacing 74 or 74LS to the 4000 series, use a 2.2kΩ resistor connected to the 5V rail. When interfacing 74 or 74LS to 74HC use a 4.7kΩ resistor.

4 Unused logic inputs
Unused inputs should not be left unconnected. Here are the rules.

Bipolar logic (74, 74LS, 74ALS)
Either: Drive the unused input from the output of an unused gated, wired so that its output is constant at logic high. This is the preferred method.

191

Or: Connect to V_{CC} (positive supply) through a $1k\Omega$ resistor; several inputs can be connected to the same resistor.

Or: Wire the input to another input of the same gate, so that both receive the same output, assuming that fanout allows this.

CMOS logic (4000, 74HC, 74HCT, 74AC, 74ACT)
Connect to V_{DD} (positive supply) or V_{SS} (ground); no resistor needed.

5 Decoupling
Sudden and extreme changes of voltage levels are an inevitable feature of digital circuits. As a result, voltage spikes generated by one device pass along the supply lines and may upset the operation of other devices. It is therefore important to decouple the supply lines from the effects of the devices they are supplying. This is generally done by connecting capacitors between the positive supply and ground (0V). Capacitors of any value between 10nF and 100nF can be used but a generally suitable value is 22nF. Such capacitors should be of the disc ceramic type. Special low-voltage capacitors are available for this purpose (p.23). There are also capacitors designed to fit under ic sockets or packages, thus providing decoupling as close as possible to the power terminals of the ic. This is important for fast-action logic (e.g. 74ALS). Under-socket capacitors are particularly useful for decoupling devices such as counters, latches and registers which are prone to supply-line interference.

Decoupling capacitors are to be scattered on the board at the rate of about 1 capacitor to every 5 logic ic's, or even 1 to 1 for the more complex ic's. In addition a board should have $1\mu F$ tantalum capacitors at the rate of 1 for every 10 ic's, or 1 for every 3 of the more complex ic's. Finally each circuit board should have a $22\mu F$ or $47\mu F$ tantalum capacitor connected close to where the power lines enter the board.

In addition to using capacitors, make the power supply tracks of a pcb as broad as possible. When laying out the board never try to run the power lines between adjacent pins of ic's, for this necessitates making the track very narrow indeed. A further source of trouble may be capacitive effects between the power line tracks and adjacent tracks on the pcb. This effect may be reduced by running three or more power line tracks in parallel, so that the outer two tracks shield the inner track or tracks from capacitive effects. Another technique is to run the positive and 0V rails close together, either adjacent on the same side of the board or on opposite sides of a double-sided board.

6 Debouncing

When a mechanical switch is opened or closed, contacts make and break several times before they eventually attain the required state. This is known as *contact bounce*. It may make little difference to level-sensitive logic but edge-sensitive logic such as counters may be triggered several times by a single switching action. The solution is to debounce the switch, as in Figure 105. This uses a non-inverting buffer from

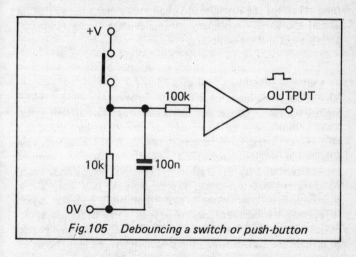

Fig.105   Debouncing a switch or push-button

an ic such as the 4050. If a normally-high output is required with a low level on pressing the button, reverse the polarity of the connections to S1 and the resistor/capacitor network, or use an inverting buffer from an ic such as the 4049.

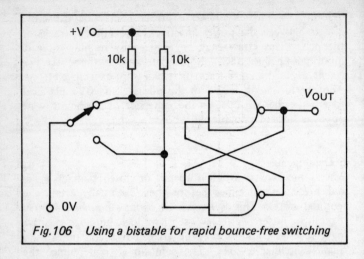

Fig.106   Using a bistable for rapid bounce-free switching

The disadvantage of the circuit in Figure 105 is that the time taken for the capacitor to charge may make the switching action too slow. A slightly more elaborate circuit (Fig.106) gives almost instant switching.

7 Analogue switches

The 4000 series includes ic's which function as switches under logical control. These are also known as *transmission gates*. Two commonly used examples are the 4016 and 4066 ic's (Fig.107). These have four switches, each of which acts as a single-pole single-throw (SPST) switch. When the control input (indicated by the dashed line) is low, the switch is open; its interterminal resistance is very high, so that only a few picoamps can flow. When the control input is high the switch is closed; its interterminal resistance then becomes about 300Ω in the 4016 or 80Ω in the 4066. Signals can be passed in either direction through the switch, provided that the signal voltage does not exceed the voltage at pin 14, and is not less than the voltage at pin 7.

The voltages applied to the power input pins depend upon the way the ic is being used:

Analogue signals: Pin 7 to −5V and pin 14 to +5V.

194

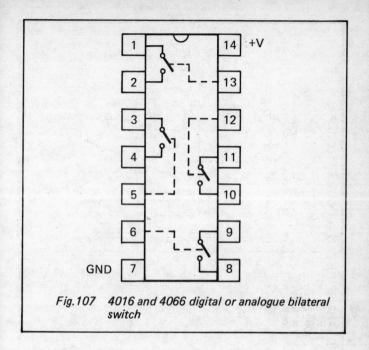

Fig.107   4016 and 4066 digital or analogue bilateral switch

Digital signals: Pin 7 to 0V and pin 14 to any voltage in the range +3V to +15V.

Switches in the same package are matched for ON resistance to within 40Ω (4016) or 5Ω (4066). The switches can pass frequencies up to 54MHz (4016) or 67MHz (4066). The switches can be turned on and off at a maximum rate of 10MHz. The total power dissipation of the ic must be kept to less than 100mW.

The four switches may be connected to each other in a variety of configurations. For example, if one terminal from each switch is connected to a common point, the switches can be used to select data or analogue signals from four different sources under logical control. Alternatively they can distribute data or signals to four different destinations.

The main difference between the two versions is that the 4066 has lower ON resistance and is preferable when switch resistance is important. However, the 4016 is preferred for

Table 14 — SERIES 4000 AND 74HC SERIES ANALOGUE SWITCHES

Device	Function	ON (Ω)	4000 Series bandwidth (MHz)	I_g (mA)	ON (Ω)	74HC Series bandwidth (MHz)	I_g (mA)
4016 74HC4016	quad SPST	200	54	10	20	100	25
4051 74HC4051	1-of-8	80	20	25	30	120	25
4052 74HC4052	dual 1-of-4	80	30	25	30	120	25
4053 74HC4053	triple 1-of-2	80	55	25	30	120	25
4066 74HC4066	quad SPST	80	67	25	15	100	25
4067	1-of-16	80	15	25	–	–	–
4097	dual 1-of-8	200	40	10	–	–	–

196

low-leakage circuits, for example, sample-and-hold circuits.

The 4000 series also includes a number of other types of analogue switch, which are summarised in Table 14. This table also lists the 74HC equivalents which have lower ON-resistances and greater bandwidth than the 4000 series. The ON-resistance is given for the operation at maximum supply voltage, and is higher if the ic is operated at lower voltages. The maximum allowable current per gate I_g is also given at maximum supply voltage, and is lower at lower voltages.

All except the 4016 and 4066 have an INHIBIT input. When this is high all switches are OFF, whatever the state of their control inputs. When control inputs are changed the switches take time to settle, and different switches may take different times. Thus several switches may be on at one time so there is an unpredictable and unallowable transition phase. If the INHIBIT is made low prior to control input changes, and then made high again, this transition phase is prevented.

A number of other analogue switches are available, of which one of the major ranges is the DG series manufactured by Siliconix. The following are examples of this series that are likely to be of interest to the home constructor:

DG200ACJ – dual SPST, ON-resistance 80Ω
DG201ACJ – quad SPST, ON-resistance 200Ω
DG202CJ – quad SPST, ON-resistance 175Ω, break-before-make
DG417DJ – single SPST switch, ON-resistance < 35Ω; low power requirements (< 35μW); control input 0 = ON, 1 = OFF; good for battery-powered projects
DG418DJ – as DG417DJ but inverse switch control
DG419DJ – single SPDT switch, otherwise as DG417DJ.

Variable resistors and capacitors

Analogue switches can be used to build resistors and capacitors which can be varied under logic control. In Figure 108 a single 4016 quadruple analogue switch is used to switch any one or more of four resistors into a circuit. The resistors are wired in series and each may be short-circuited by one of the analogue switches. The resistors are weighted on a binary scale so that we can obtain all values between zero and 15R in

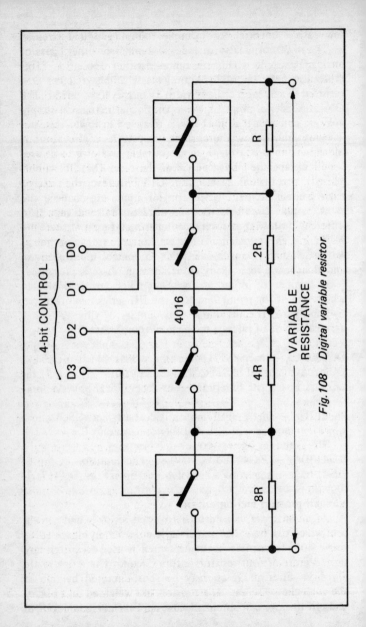

Fig. 108 *Digital variable resistor*

steps of R. This ignores the on-resistance of the switches themselves, which is typically 580Ω when the ic is operated on a 5V supply. This resistance may be reduced to 250Ω by operating the ic on ±5V or a single supply of 10V. It is reduced to 200Ω on a ±7.5V or +15V supply. Provided that R is of the order of tens of kilohms the error due to on-resistance may be ignored. If R must have a relatively low value, use one of the ic's with low on-resistance (see tables in previous section). If the circuit in which the variable resistor is to be used would be damaged by a very low resistance (i.e. all switches closed), precautions against this must be taken when designing the control circuit.

A similar circuit is used to switch paralleled capacitors (Fig.109), allowing capacitances in the range C (*not* zero) to 15C. In this circuit an error arises owing to gate capacitance, so the circuit is unsuitable when C is only a few tens of picofarads.

8 Complex logic functions

Often a complex logic function can be obtained by using a network of individual logic gates but occasionally it is simpler to use the technique described here. This makes use of the complex logic already provided by the ic. It also has the advantage that the function can be readily changed. This can be done simply by re-wiring the inputs. By arranging the inputs to be electronically controlled, the circuit can produce any one out of several different sets of outputs.

The circuit in Figure 110 is based on a multiplexer (or data-selector) ic such as the 74151, but other multiplexers can be used, including a 16-line to 1-line multiplexer for 4-bit logic functions. However, there is a way of using an 8-line multiplexer for 4-bit functions, as explained later.

As an example, consider the 3-bit function set out in the truth table on page 201. The function is simply obtained by setting out the truth table and then connecting the inputs 0 to 7 of the multiplexer to the supply line (for $Z = 1$) or to the 0V line (for $Z = 0$) as shown in the figure. Then if, for example the select inputs are set to '011' (address 3), the data present at input 3, namely a '0' appears at the output Z.

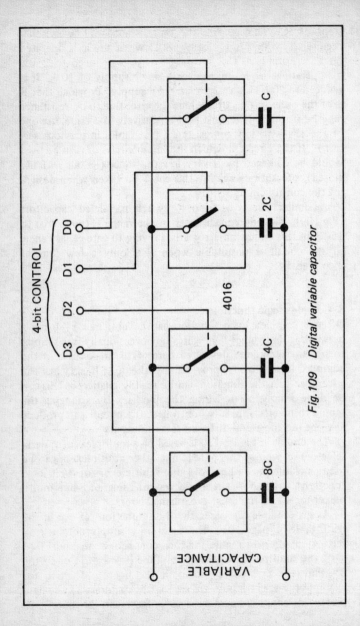

Fig. 109   Digital variable capacitor

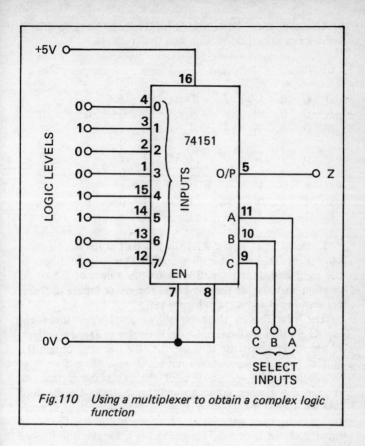

Fig.110   Using a multiplexer to obtain a complex logic
function

	Inputs		Output
C	B	A	Z
0	0	0	0
0	0	1	1
0	1	0	0
0	1	1	0
1	0	0	1
1	0	1	1
1	1	0	0
1	1	1	1

The same ic can be used for 4-bit functions by using what is known as a *folded table*. Consider this truth table:

Inputs				Output	Inputs				Output	Req'd output
D	C	B	A	Z	D	C	B	A	Z	
0	0	0	0	0	1	0	0	0	0	0
0	0	0	1	1	1	0	0	1	1	1
0	0	1	0	0	1	0	1	0	1	D
0	0	1	1	0	1	0	1	1	0	$\underline{0}$
0	1	0	0	1	1	1	0	0	0	$\overline{D}$
0	1	0	1	1	1	1	0	1	0	$\overline{D}$
0	1	1	0	0	1	1	1	0	0	0
0	1	1	1	1	1	1	1	1	1	1

Columns C, B, A and Z of the left half of the table are the same as in the 3-bit table above, while D is 0 for all lines. In the right half, D is 1 on all lines and the values of Z bear no relation to those in the left half. The select inputs of the ic are set to C, B and A, as in Figure 110.

The first line of the table shows that, when the select inputs are 000 we require Z = 0. The value of D has no effect. If the '0' input of the ic is wired to 0V, we shall obtain the correct result for inputs 0000 and 1000.

Similarly, the second line of the table shows that we require Z = 1 when inputs are 0001 and 1001. On the third line we need 0 for input 0010 and 1 for input 1010. Z needs to have the *same value* as D. Thus we ensure this by wiring input 2 of the ic to the D line (Fig.111). On the fifth line we need 1 for input 0100 and 0 for input 1100. This is the inverse of D, so we wire input 4 of the ic to the inverted D line. The right-hand column of the table summarises the wiring required to produce this 4-bit function.

9 Bistables

These are also known as *flip-flops*, of which there are several kinds.

(i) S-R flip-flops: A simple type of *set−reset* flip-flop consists of two cross-connected NAND or NOR gates (Fig.112).

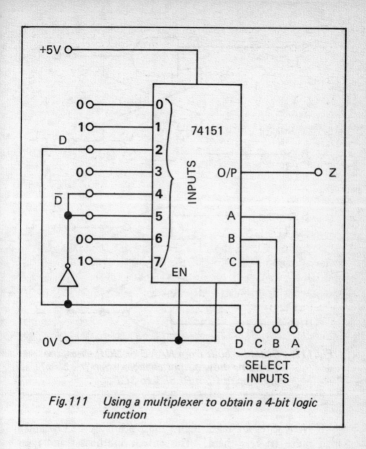

Fig.111 *Using a multiplexer to obtain a 4-bit logic function*

In the NAND type the two inputs are held high and the flip-flop is set or reset by a brief low pulse on one of the inputs. Once set, the flip-flop stays in that state, even if subsequent pulses arrive on the SET input. It thus acts as a 'memory', its state depending on which of its inputs last received a low pulse.

The inputs may be held high by previous logic circuitry, or by a pull-up resistor connected to the positive supply. A push-button can be used to short-circuit the input to 0V for setting or resetting.

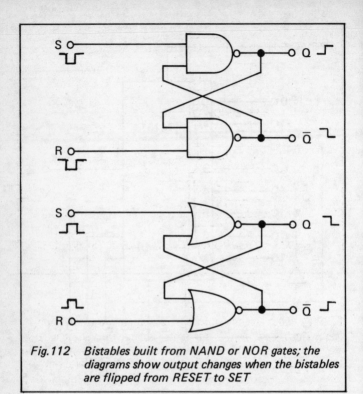

Fig.112 Bistables built from NAND or NOR gates; the diagrams show output changes when the bistables are flipped from RESET to SET

If NOR gates are used, inputs must normally be low and a high pulse triggers them. The output in the set and reset states are the opposite of those for a NAND gate flip-flop.

Ready-built S-R flip-flops are available in integrated form, as listed in the table on p.210.

In the *unclocked* flip-flops described so far, the change in output occurs immediately the pulse arrives. A *clocked* S-R flip-flop has an additional input which receives a clocking signal. The change does not occur until the next clock pulse appears. Such a flip-flop can be built from a J-K flip-flop as explained in (iv) below.

(ii) T-type flip-flops: T-type or *toggle-type* flip-flops have a single input, usually referred to as the CLOCK input (Fig.

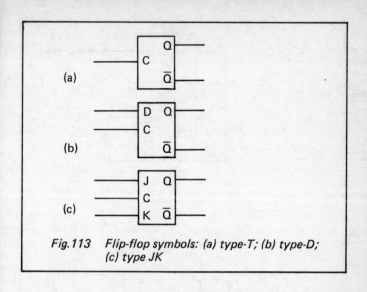

Fig.113   Flip-flop symbols: (a) type-T; (b) type-D; (c) type JK

113(a)). They have two outputs which are always in opposite states (high—low or low—high) and change every time a clocking pulse arrives at the input. Thus two clock pulses return the flip-flop to its original state. Putting this in other words, the outputs change state at exactly half the clock frequency T-type flip-flops are usually built from D-type or JK-type flip-flops as described below.

(iii) D-type flip-flops: D-type or *delay-type* flip-flops have a single DATA input, a CLOCK input and two outputs (Fig. 113(b)). They may also have SET and RESET inputs to set or reset the flip-flop instantly without waiting for the clock. The SET input is sometimes called the PRESET input, and the RESET input the CLEAR. Data (high or low) that is present at the D input appears at the Q output on the *next* high-going clock pulse, so there is a delay between the time when the data is sent to the flip-flop and the time it appears at the output. In most types of ic, the transition occurs on the *rising edge* of the pulse, but there are some TTL ic's (e.g. 7476A) in which it occurs on the negative edge. The inverse data appears at the $\overline{Q}$ output.

205

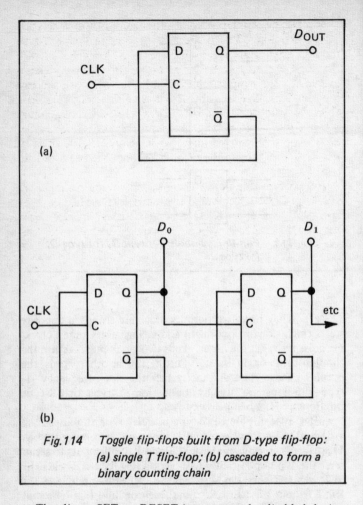

(a)

(b)

Fig.114   Toggle flip-flops built from D-type flip-flop:
(a) single T flip-flop; (b) cascaded to form a
binary counting chain

The direct SET or RESET inputs must be disabled during
normal clocked operation of the ic. In CMOS types (e.g.
4013) these terminals are to be held low. Making the SET
input high forces Q high and $\overline{Q}$ low. SET and RESET inputs
must not both be activated at the same time. With TTL (e.g.
7474) SET and RESET are to be held high and are active when
made low.

If a D-type flip-flop is wired as in Figure 114(a), it acts as a T-type flip-flop. This is the usual way of making a T-type flip-flop as they are not available as ic's. A number of such flip-flops chained together (Fig.114(b)) form a binary counting chain. The number represented by the outputs of successive flip-flops increments by 1 each time the clock goes high. Of course, the clock need not be a *regularly* repeating circuit. It can, for example, be a light sensor which gives a high output every time the light reaching it is interrupted. The chain of flip-flops then counts the number of times the beam of light is broken.

(iv) JK-type flip-flops: These have two control inputs (J and K), a CLOCK input, and two outputs (Fig.113(c)). They may also have direct-acting SET and RESET inputs. What happens when the clock pulse arrives depends upon the logic levels present at the J and K inputs:

J	K	Outputs	
		Q	$\bar{Q}$
0	0	No change	
0	1	1	0
1	0	0	1
1	1	Change to opposite state	

The first 3 lines of this table show the response required for a clocked S-R flip-flop. The fourth line shows the response of a T-type flip-flop (Fig.114).

J-K flip-flops are available in different versions: some are triggered by a rising edge (see p.210) while others are triggered by a falling edge. Some have multiple J and K inputs; for example, the 7470 has three J inputs and three K inputs. Of the J inputs, J1 and J2 are non-inverted but J3 is inverted. These inputs are ANDed together to give the value of J referred to in the table above. Thus J1 and J2 must both be high and J3 must be low to obtain the functions of the lower two lines of the table. The same applies to the K inputs. If this logic is not required, the operation is simplified by wiring some of the inputs permanently high or low, or an ic with single JK inputs is used.

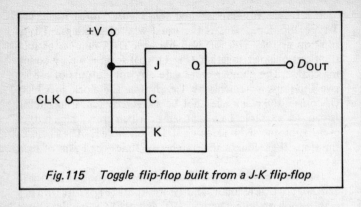

Fig.115   Toggle flip-flop built from a J-K flip-flop

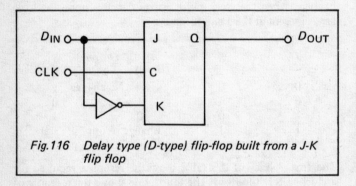

*Fig.116   Delay type (D-type) flip-flop built from a J-K
flip flop*

Figure 115 shows how to convert a JK flip-flop into a T-type flip-flop, if a simple toggling action is required. The JK flip-flop can also be converted to a D-type flip-flop, as in Figure 116.   Several of these can be built into a counting chain.

A simple 1-bit memory

A JK flip-flop can be used as a memory unit by connecting it as in Figure 117. The flip-flop can be either TTL (7473) or CMOS (4027). The SET input of the 4027 is not used; hold this low. The circuit is reset by a pulse on the RESET line, low for the 7473, high for the 4027. The Q output then goes low. The trigger input is normally low but, if this is taken

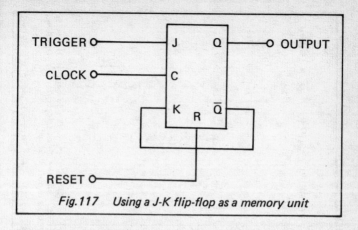

Fig.117   Using a J-K flip-flop as a memory unit

high, the Q output goes high on the next low-going (7473) or high-going (4027) clock pulse. The output stays high until the flip-flop is reset. The trigger input must be held until the next active clock edge occurs. If the inverse output is required, use the $\overline{Q}$ output.

Choosing flip-flops
A very wide range of ic's is available; Table 15 will help you select the one you require. Devices numbered 74XX are more readily available as 74LSXX, 74HCXX or 74HCTXX.

10 Monostables

1 Simple pulse generators
Often we need a short pulse to trigger a device, to step on a counter or perform some other operation in which the exact length of the pulse is immaterial within limits. The simplest way of providing such a pulse is a half monostable. Figure 118 shows two half monostables using the non-inverting 4016 buffer and the inverting 40106 buffer, both with Schmitt trigger inputs. TTL buffers can be used instead, such as the 7414 inverting buffer. It is also possible to use a NAND gate with Schmitt trigger inputs,

Table 15 – FLIP-FLOPS

F-F Type	Device No.	Pins	F-Fs	Clocking	SET	RESET	ENABLE	$\overline{Q}$	3-state
S-R	74118	16	6	—	L	LC	—	—	—
	74LS279	16	4	—	L*	L	—	—	—
	4043	16	4	—	H	H	—	—	H
	4044	16	4	—	L	L	—	—	H
D	7474	14	2	↑	L	LC	—	Y	—
	74174	16	6	↑	—	LC	—	—	—
	74175	16	4	↑	—	LC	—	Y	—
	74273	20	8	↑	—	LC	—	—	—
	74374	20	8	↑	—	—	LC	—	L
	74377	20	8	↑	—	—	LC	—	—
	74378	16	6	↑	—	—	LC	—	—
	74379	16	4	↑	—	—	LC	Y	—
	4013	14	2	↑	H	H	—	Y	—
JK	7470+	14	1	↑	L	L	—	Y	—
	7472+	14	1	H	—	L	—	Y	—
	7473	14	2	↓	—	L	—	Y	—
	7476	16	2	↓	L	L	—	Y	—
	74109+	16	2	↑	L	L	—	Y	—
	4027	16	2	↑	H	H	—	Y	—

Clocking: L = low pulse; H = high pulse; ↑ = rising edge; ↓ = falling edge. SET: L = sets with a low input; H = sets with a high input. RESET: L, H as for SET; C = common reset. ENABLE: L = enables clock triggering; C = common enable. $\overline{Q}$: Y = $\overline{Q}$ outputs accessible. 3-state: L = low enables output; H = high enables output.
* 2 flip-flops have 2 SET inputs; both H = H, one or both L = L.
+ For 7470, J = J1.J2.J3, K = K1.K2.$\overline{K3}$ For 7472, J = J1.J2.J3, K = K1.K2.K3   For 74109, K input is inverted.

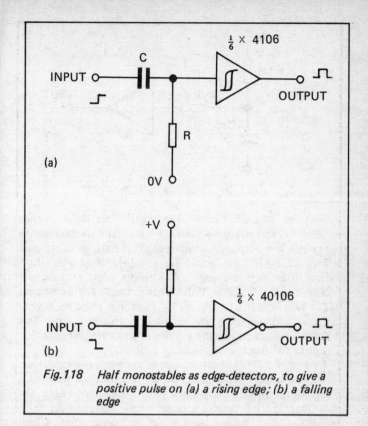

*Fig.118 Half monostables as edge-detectors, to give a
positive pulse on (a) a rising edge; (b) a falling
edge*

wiring the inputs together to convert the gate to the INVERT
function. The ic's required are 74132 (TTL) or 4093 (CMOS).

Figure 119 shows a circuit which produces a high pulse for
almost 1 second when power is switched on. This may be used
to reset microprocessors and other circuit units which require
to be reset when power is first applied to them. The duration
of the pulse is given by $t = 0.7RC$; with the values shown, the
pulse lasts 0.7s.

Some slightly more complex pulse generators are shown in
Figure 120. They allow the pulse length to be determined
more exactly and allow for longer pulses than the circuits
above. The circuit at (a) has a normally high output and gives

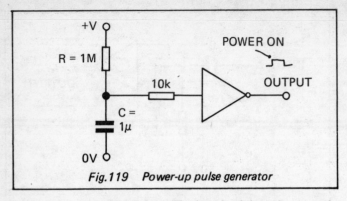

Fig.119   Power-up pulse generator

a low pulse on a rising edge. The length of the pulse depends on R and C and is approximately $t = RC$. The arrangement in (b) gives a low output on a falling edge. If NOR gates are used instead of NAND in circuits (a) and (b), we obtain a high output pulse, on a rising and a falling edge, respectively.

The circuit of Figure 120(c) makes use of the delay time of the two inverters to give a very short high pulse every time the input changes from low to high or from high to low. This is a good way of producing a series of short triggering pulses. The circuit also acts as a frequency doubler.

In Figure 120(d) the function of circuits (a) and (b) are combined, using only 3 gates. Output 1 gives a low pulse on a rising edge; output 2 gives a low pulse on a falling edge. The pulse lengths are independently set by the values of R1 × C1 and R2 × C2. Each generator has an enable input; a high input enables the generator; a low input inhibits it (output high). If the enabling function is not required the inputs can be tied to the positive supply (through a 1kΩ resistor if TTL is being used).

2 Precision pulse generators

One of the configurations of the 4047 retriggerable monostable is shown in Figure 121. This gives both positive and negative output pulses when triggered by a positive-going edge. The output is extended if the input is retriggered, by a positive-going edge at pin 12. The pulse length is given by $t = 2.48RC$. R is between 10kΩ and 1MΩ. C must be greater

212

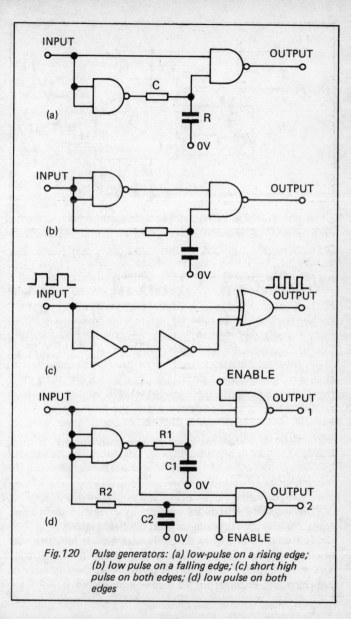

Fig.120 Pulse generators: (a) low-pulse on a rising edge;
(b) low pulse on a falling edge; (c) short high
pulse on both edges; (d) low pulse on both
edges

213

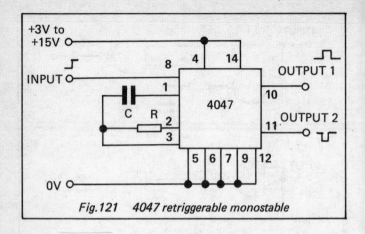

Fig.121   4047 retriggerable monostable

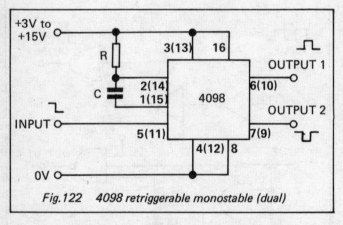

Fig.122   4098 retriggerable monostable (dual)

than 1nF; polarised capacitors should not be used.

This monostable may be triggered by a negative-going edge, using pin 6 as the trigger input. Pin 8 is held high.

The 4098 is a dual monostable with similar facilities. As wired in Figure 122, it is triggerable on a negative-going edge and is retriggerable. For other configurations the connections are (figures in brackets are the second monostable):

214

Positive-edge (retriggerable):
    pins 3 (13), 5 (11), 16 to supply
    pin 8 to 0V
    input to pin 4 (12)

Positive-edge (non-retriggerable):
    pins 3 (13), 16 to supply
    pin 8 to 0V
    input to pin 4 (12)
    join pin 5 (11) to pin 7 (9)

Negative-edge (not retriggerable):
    pins 3 (13), 16 to supply
    pin 8 to 0V
    input to pin 5 (11)
    join pin 4 (12) to pin 6 (10)

If either section is unused, connect pin 5 (11) to the supply, and pins 3 and 4 (12 and 13) to 0V. The output pulse lasts for RC seconds where R is between $1k\Omega$ and $10M\Omega$ and C is between 10pF and $100\mu F$.

The 4541 programmable astable can also be used as a monostable, as explained on p.222.

11 Astables

Two-transistor astable

The circuit of Figure 123 is a simple astable based on an *npn* and a *pnp* transistor. It is suited for flashing an LED, or a low-voltage (e.g. 6V) filament lamp. If the load consists of a loudspeaker the sound emitted depends on frequency. At low frequency (C1 = $10\mu F$, for example) individual clicks are heard as the circuit changes state, making the circuit useful as a metronome. At high frequency (C1 = 10nF for example) the clicks merge to give an audio frequency tone. The loudspeaker can either be of relatively high impedance (e.g. 64Ω) or a low-impedance (e.g. 8Ω) speaker can be used in series with a current-limiting resistor ($5-39\Omega$). TR2 must be rated to carry the load current, the maximum value of which may be approximately calculated from:

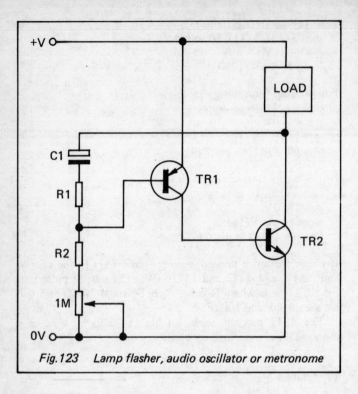

Fig.123   Lamp flasher, audio oscillator or metronome

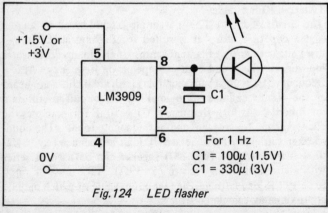

Fig.124   LED flasher

$$I = (V_{\text{SUPPLY}} - 0.6)/R_L$$

If necessary, use a medium-power or high-power transistor for TR2. Frequency depends on the ratio between R1 and R2 (R2 > R1), and the value of C1. The variable resistor is used to adjust frequency, but may be omitted if only a fixed frequency is required.

The LM3909

This ic has a number of uses as the basis of oscillator circuits. One of its special applications is as a low-current LED flasher (Fig.124). The ic does not merely switch the LED on and off, but discharges the capacitor rapidly through it to produce an extra-bright flash. The circuit is powered by a 1.5V cell or a 3V battery and, with the capacitor values shown, flashes at about 1Hz. For lower power consumption, with a shorter but still very conspicuous flash at about 1Hz, make an additional connection between pin 1 and pin 8 use a 330μF capacitor and a 1.5V cell. A size **AA** alkaline cell lasts for about 6 months of continuous running.

Two-gate TTL astable

Two inverting TTL gates, connected as in Figure 125 are a convenient way of making a simple astable. With 1kΩ resistors frequency may be in the range 3Hz to 3MHz,

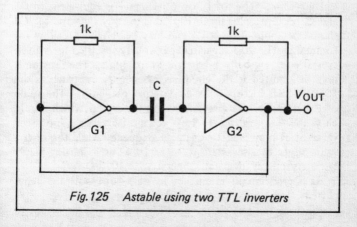

Fig.125   Astable using two TTL inverters

217

depending on the value of the capacitor:

$$f = \frac{7.7 \times 10^{-4}}{C}$$

NAND or NOR gates with their inputs wired together may be substituted for the inverters (p.182). If NAND gates are used, it is possible to provide an inhibit input using one of the inputs of gate G1 (the other input being connected to the output of G2, as in the figure). If the enable input is taken high, the astable oscillates; if it is taken low the action is inhibited, with the output of G1 high and the output of G2 low. Usually an inactive-low output is preferred as this reduces current consumption by subsequent circuits. However, it is possible to provide an inactive-high output by using one of the inputs of G2 as the enable input.

Crystal oscillators
Two types of crystal oscillator are the parallel-resonant and the series-resonant circuits of Figure 126. The inverters are CMOS inverter gates or, alternatively, NAND or NOR gates with their inputs wired together.

The parallel circuit has the advantage that it takes very little current (only about $1\mu A$) but it has relatively slow starting time. The total load capacitance is equivalent to C1 and C2 in series plus up to 10pF due to stray capacitance. C2 should be about 3 times C1 and may be variable to allow for trimming. The load capacitance is usually specified for a given crystal and is usually in the region of 30pF. The resistor R may be omitted if the circuit is based on an ic (such as the 4060) which incorporates an internal oscillator. The value of R determines the level of drive to the crystal, which should be in the region of 0.5 to 1mW for most crystals. Too low a value of R may lead to unstable frequency while too high a value leads to slow starting. Try $10k\Omega$ as a starting value. Use a crystal cut for parallel operation.

The series circuit is quicker to start but requires a higher current. Use a crystal cut for series operation.

When laying out either circuit as a pcb, it is important to

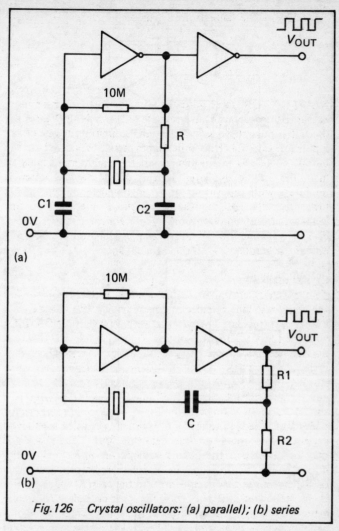

Fig.126   Crystal oscillators: (a) parallel); (b) series

avoid stray capacitance across the crystal. One technique is
to provide a loop of track around the terminals of the crystal
and to ground this. Also avoid running the tracks of the
oscillator too close to those of other parts of the circuit.

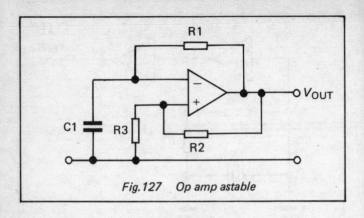

Fig. 127   Op amp astable

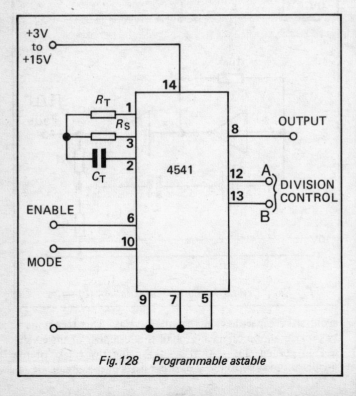

Fig. 128   Programmable astable

Op amp astable

The circuit of Figure 127 is an astable with 50% duty cycle and a frequency independent of supply voltage. The op amp chosen should have wide swing, fast slew rate and low input bias current. The frequency is given by:

$$f = \frac{1}{2R1 \times C1 \times \log_e\left(\dfrac{R2 + 2R3}{R2}\right)}$$

Programmable astable

The 4541 ic (Fig.128) incorporates a clock and a programmable divider. This has the advantage that, since the clock can run at relatively high frequency, the timing capacitor can be of low value. This makes it feasible to use high-precision capacitors. Also the lower frequencies can be obtained without having to resort to the use of electrolytic capacitors, which are unstable in value.

Clock frequency is set in the range 1kHz to 100kHz by the values of R_T and C_T:

$$f = \frac{1}{2.3 \, R_T C_T}$$

R_T is between 5kΩ and 1MΩ, R_S is twice R_T. C_T is between 100pF and 100nF. The division of the clock frequency is controlled by the logical inputs A and B.

Input		Divide by
A	B	
0	0	8192
0	1	1024
1	0	256
1	1	65536

Thus with clock frequency of 1kHz and both A and B high, the output frequency is 0.0152, or once every 65.5s. A slightly lower frequency could be used in a minutes timer.

221

Pin 6 is the ENABLE input; taking this high resets the counter and the output at pin 8 goes low. Make pin 6 low to enable the count. However, the output is inverted if pin 9 is made high instead of low, as in the figure. With pin 9 high, output goes high on resetting.

Pin 10 allows for two modes of operation. With pin 10 high, the counter runs continuously but, with the pin low, counting stops when the output has passed through 1 complete cycle. This allows the ic to be used as a monostable. It is started again by a low pulse applied to pin 6.

Voltage-controlled oscillators
Two function generators with voltage-controlled frequency are described on pp.155 and 157.

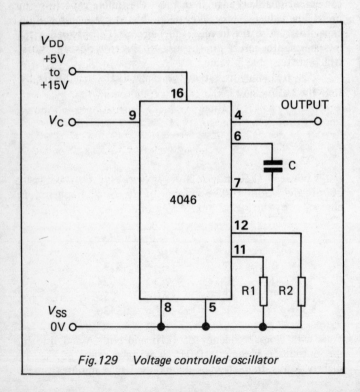

Fig. 129   Voltage controlled oscillator

The 4046 phase locked loop ic has a VCO which is easy to use (Fig.129), and generates a square wave from 0Hz to 500kHz, with 50% duty cycle. If pin 12 (Fig.129) is left unconnected (R2 = ∞), and $V_C = V_{DD}/2$, it runs at its central frequency, f_0 :

$$f_0 = \frac{1}{R1 \times C}$$

This applies when V_{DD} is 15V. Frequency is slightly lower for lower supply voltages. R1 must be between 10kΩ and 1MΩ. C must be greater than 50pF (add 32pF for input capacitance with low values of C). As V_C is swept from 0V to V_{DD}, frequency sweeps from 0Hz to $2f_0$. The relationship is approximately linear if V_C is more than 2V, but the frequency-voltage curve is flatter toward the lower end of the range. Below 2V, it is unsafe to rely upon obtaining a given frequency precisely. Linearity is best if C > 1nF and R1 > 100kΩ.

If R2 is included, the frequency range is offset. Given f_0 and the half-range f_r, the range extends from $f_{min} = f_0 - f_r$ to $f_{max} = f_0 + f_r$. An approximate calculation is as follows; again, this is not reliable for $V_C < 2$:

(a)   Calculate R2 = a/($f_{min} \times$ C), where a = 1 if V_{DD} = 5, and a = 2 for V_{DD} > 10.

(b)   Calculate f_{max}/f_{min} and look up the corresponding value of b in this table:

f_{max}/f_{min}	b
2	1.00
3	0.40
4	0.25
5	0.17
6	0.13
8	0.10
10	0.09
20	0.03
40	0.02

(c)   Calculate R1 = R2 × b.

Example: For f_0 = 10kHz, f_r = 8kHz, with C = 1nF, and V_{DD} = 10. f_{min} = 2kHz, f_{max} = 18kHz.

(a) R2 = $2/(2 \times 10^3 \times 1 \times 10^{-9})$ = 1MΩ
(b) f_{max}/f_{min} = 18/2 = 9. b = 0.1
(c) R1 = R2 × 0.1 = 100kΩ.

12 Timers

The classic timer ic is the 555, now produced in various versions, all of which have the same action. The basic circuits are the monostable (Fig.130) and the astable (Fig.131). The latter is normally operated *without* the diodes shown in the figure.

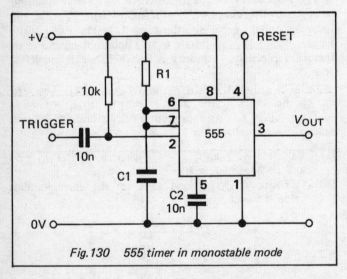

Fig.130   *555 timer in monostable mode*

In the monostable, the reset input may be permanently wired to the supply, and is then inoperative. If the reset facility is required, connect the reset input as in Figure 132. The monostable is triggered by a negative-going pulse which takes the input voltage below 1/3 of the supply voltage. To end the trigger pulse, the input must be returned above 1/3 supply voltage.

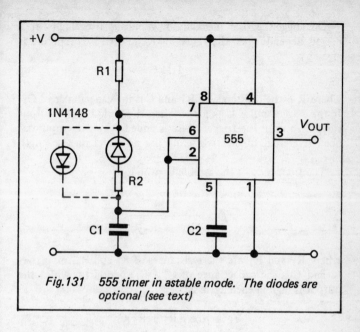

Fig.131   555 timer in astable mode. The diodes are
optional (see text)

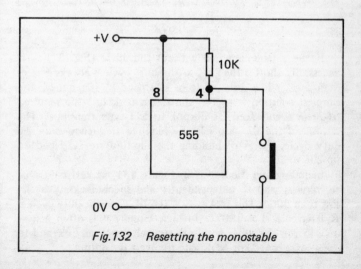

Fig.132   Resetting the monostable

225

On triggering, the normally low output rises high for a period depending on the values of R1 and C1. The period is given by:

$$t = 1.1RC$$

where R is the resistance of R1 and C is the capacitance of C1. If the trigger pulse lasts longer than the period t, the output stays high until the trigger pulse is ended. Once the input has been triggered, further triggering has no effect on the length of t.

The frequency of the astable is given by:

$$f = \frac{1.44}{(R_1 + 2R_2)C}$$

where R_1 and R_2 are the resistances of R1 and R2 respectively and C is the capacitance of C1. The period for which the output is high in each cycle is:

$$t_1 = 0.69(R_1 + R_2)C$$

The period for which the output is low is given by:

$$t_2 = 0.69R_2C$$

If the astable is wired without the diode (Fig.131) t_2 is necessarily shorter than t_1, so the duty cycle is always greater than 50%. If a duty cycle of *exactly* 50% is required, the simplest solution is to run the timer at double the required frequency and feed its output to a T-type flip-flop. The output of the flip-flop has the required frequency and 50% duty cycle. Ways of building the flip-flop are described on pp.206 to 208.

Including the diodes, as in Figure 131, makes it possible to vary t_1 and t_2 independently and so obtain duty cycles less than 50%. This makes $t_1 = 0.69R_1C$, so the duty cycle is $R_1/(R_1 + R_2) \times 100\%$. In logic circuits it is often just as easy to run the timer with a duty cycle less than 50% and to use a spare NAND or NOR gate to invert the output.

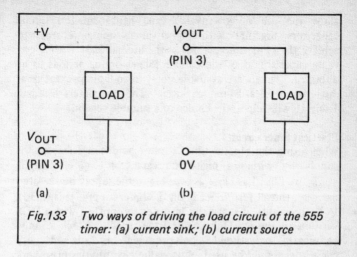

Fig.133 Two ways of driving the load circuit of the 555 timer: (a) current sink; (b) current source

The output of the timer ic can be used to source or sink current (Fig.133). As a current source, the monostable supplies current to the load (e.g. energises a relay coil) during the timed 'high output' period. As a current sink, the timer draws current through the load *except* during this period. Outputs are compatible with TTL and CMOS logic.

Several other timer ic's are obtainable but the details of their operation are too specific to be detailed here. Among those of particular interest is the ZN1034E, which incorporates a divider so that it can generate periods from 16ms to several days in length. The bipolar 2240 timer and its CMOS version, the 7240, are two other timers capable of very long periods; they can also generate a variety of pulse patterns when used in the astable mode. The TMS1601ANL is a dedicated microcomputer timer capable of generating the signals for an LED or LCD numeric display and can be programmed to control up to 4 outputs by time of day on a weekly basis.

Selecting an ic from the 555 family
The original bipolar 555 timer is a robust device. Its main disadvantage is that its switching generates large spikes on the supply lines. The CMOS versions require less current and

allow the use of lower-value (and hence smaller) timing capacitors together with higher-value timing resistors to achieve the same time periods as the bipolar 555. With larger-value capacitors they allow much longer timing periods to be obtained. Timers are available singly in an 8-pin package or as dual timers in a 14-pin package. The parameters listed in Table 16 will help in the choice of a suitable version.

Practical timer circuits

When using the bipolar timer it must be decoupled from the supply by wiring a high-value capacitor (e.g. electrolytic $10\mu F$ to $100\mu F$) as close as possible to the supply pins. Alternatively, thread ferrite beads on the timer supply leads (p.30). In both circuits, it is usually in order to omit C2 with CMOS versions of the ic. Only low-leakage capacitors such as poly-carbonate, polystyrene, polypropylene or silvered mica capacitors should be used. Low-value electrolytics may work fairly well but the value required must be found by trial as (a) leakage, and (b) poor tolerance, mean that timing periods are unpredictable. They are also likely to change as the capacitance changes due to age and use. Ceramic disc capacitors should not be used as they are unstable at high frequencies.

The minimum recommended values for R1 and R2 are $5k\Omega$ and $3k\Omega$ respectively with the bipolar 555. With CMOS choose large-value resistors and small-value capacitors, so as to minimise current requirements and power dissipation. The use of a resistor and capacitor on the trigger input is a convenient way of interfacing the ic to a triggering circuit, but a direct connection can be used if the correct input voltage levels are provided.

13 Latches and registers

Latches and registers act as memory units. One type of latch is the S-R flip-flop described on page 202. Another type is the single latch built from 4 NAND gates (e.g. a 7400 or 4011) and an inverter (Fig.134). A latch has a control input, known as ENABLE, STORE or CLOCK. When input is enabled the Q output follows the DATA input, changing as it changes. The $\overline{Q}$ output is the inverse of the DATA input. When input

Table 16 – SELECTING AN IC FROM THE 555 FAMILY

Single timer	Dual timer	Supply voltage	Quiescent current*	Load sink	Current source	Trig current	Max. frequency	Precision+
555	556	4.5 – 16	3mA/5	200mA	200mA	0.5µA	–	1%
7555	7556	2 – 18	120µA/18	100mA	100mA	10nA	>500kHz	2%
TLC555C	TLC556	2 – 18	360µA/15	100mA	10mA	20pA	2MHz	–

* per timer/at supply voltage quoted
+ in monostable mode; also depends on precision and stability of R1 and C1.

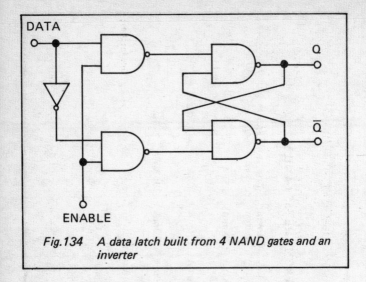

DATA

ENABLE

*Fig.134   A data latch built from 4 NAND gates and an
inverter*

is disabled, the outputs of the latch remain unchanged, or
latched, in the state they held at that instant. Such latches
are available as integrated circuits. For example, the 7475 has
four latches of this kind arranged as two pairs with common
ENABLE inputs. Other latches are listed in the table on
page 231.

D-type flip-flops (p.205) can also be used as latches, but
differ from the above in that they do not have a state in
which the output follows the data input. They are *clocked*
latches and the output changes only at the appropriate clock
edge.

When a number of latches share common clocking, we
refer to them as *registers*. In *storage registers* the latches are
arranged so as to sample and hold several bits of data
simultaneously. Several ic's of this sort are available (see
below). In *shift registers* the latches are connected in a chain,
with provision for shifting the data along the chain. Shift
registers are described in more detail on p.232.

Choosing latches and storage registers

Table 17 is a guide to the selection of the most suitable ic.

Table 17 – CHOOSING LATCHES AND STORAGE REGISTERS

Device No.	Pins	Bits	Latching or Store	RESET	ENABLE	ADD	$\bar{Q}$	3-state
7475	16	4	L (2 + 2)	–	–	–	Y	–
7477	14	4	L (2 + 2)	–	–	–	–	–
74173	16	4	↑	H	LL	–	–	LL
74259	16	8	H	L	–	Y	–	–
74298	16	4*	H	–	–	–	–	L
74373+	20	8	L	–	–	–	–	–
74398	20	4*	L	–	–	–	Y	–
74399	16	4*	L	–	–	–	–	–
4042	16	4	LH	–	–	–	Y	–
4076	16	4	↑	H	LL	–	–	LL
4099	16	8	L	–	–	Y	–	–
4508	24	4 + 4**	L + L	H + H	–	–	–	L + L

LATCHING: L = L latches; H = high latches; LH = polarity selectable; ↑ = rising edge latches; ↓ = falling edge latches;
L+L = 2 independent latches.
RESET: L = low pulse resets; H = high pulse resets; H+H = 2 independent latches.
ENABLE: LL = two inputs, *both* L to latch on ↑ clock.
ADD (REASSABLE): Y = latches addressable for input and output.
$\bar{Q}$: Y = $\bar{Q}$ output accessible.
3-state: L = enable output; LL = two inputs, both L, enables output.
L+L = two independent latches.

* 2-port register; selects and stores data from two 4-bit sources. ** two independently controlled 4-bit registers.
+ 74533 is the same, but with inverted outputs.

231

Shift registers

These are used for processing data, and may also be used as a delay line. The registers described in this section are all *static registers*, which retain their data indefinitely. Also available are *dynamic registers* which process a large number of bits, but need to be refreshed regularly. Registers may be loaded either in series or in parallel, some registers provide one facility, some provide the other and a few can operate in either mode. Similarly, registers have serial or parallel output. Shifting normally takes place to the right (from input to output) but some registers have a left-shift mode. Different ic's have different combinations of the above features (SIPO, PIPO, etc.) and it is usually possible to find one which will suit the circuit. However, there are constraints resulting from the number of pins on a package of reasonable size; for example, the 4031 64-bit register is SISO. A selection table appears on page 233.

Shift registers can be constructed from JK flip-flops as shown in Figure 135.

Pseudo-random number generator

A shift register is used to generate a long but regularly repeating sequence of high and low bits. Given a long enough register, the sequence repeats so infrequently that it is effectively random. The circuit requires a shift register with two of its inputs fed to an exclusive-OR gate, the output of which is fed back to the data input of the register (Fig.136). The register is driven by a clock. To produce a sequence which does not latch into an 'all zero' state, and which does not recur along the register, the feedback may only be taken from certain stages. Given a register length m, with feedback from stage m and an earlier stage n, the sequence lengths are as in the examples in Table 19.

Note that sequence length is 2^{m-1}. If the clock is run at high frequency, the output from the circuit may be used as a source of 'white noise'.

232

Table 18 – CHOOSING SHIFT REGISTERS

Device No.	Pins	Bits	Input/Output	Shift	Load	RESET	L/R	$\bar{Q}$
7495	14	4	PIPO, SIPO	→	H	–	LR	–
7496	16	5	PIPO, SIPO	↑	HI	L	R	–
74164	14	8	SIPO*	↑	–	L	R	Y
74165	16	8	PISO, SISO	↑+	LI	–	R	Y
74166	16	8	PISO, SISO	↑+	L	L	R	–
74194	16	4	PIPO, SIPO	↑	HH	L	LR	–
74195	16	4	PIPO, SIPO**	→	L	L	R	–
4006	14	18++	SISO	→	–	–	R	–
4014	16	8 (6, 7)	PISO, SISO	↑	H	–	R	–
4015	16	4 + 4	SIPO, SISO	↑	–	H	R	–
4021	16	8 (6, 7)	PISO, SISO	↑	HI	–	R	–
4031	16	64	SISO	↑	–	–	R	–
4035	16	4	PIPO, SIPO**	↑	H	H	R	X

Bits: (6, 7) means outputs of stages 6 and 7 also accessible.   Input/Output: PO implies SO also.
Load: Data transferred to latches on next clock edge, except for I = immediate load.
L/R = Left and/or right shift.
$\bar{Q}$: Y = $\bar{Q}$ output available; X = COMPLEMENT input, when H gives Q output instead of Q.
* two serial inputs, A and B, $both$ H input.
** JK serial inputs.
+ clock inhibit input (H inhibits)
++ independent 4+4+5+5 stages give registers of various lengths; bit 4 of 5-stage registers also accessible.

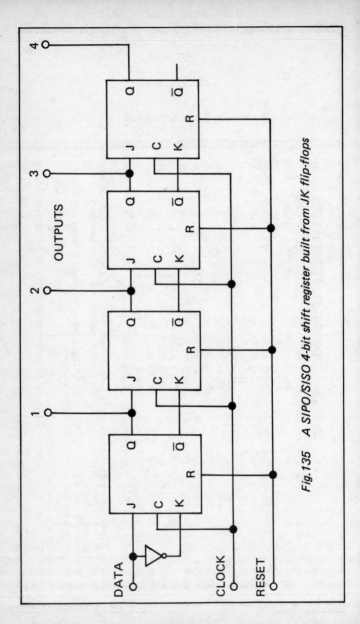

Fig. 135   A SIPO/SISO 4-bit shift register built from JK flip-flops

234

Table 19

No. of stages m	Feedback also from stage n	Length of sequence
3	2	7
4	3	15
5	3	31
6	5	63
7	6	127
8*	4, 5, 6	255
9	5	511
10	7	1023
11	9	2047
15	14	32767
16*	4, 13, 15	65535

* these require 3 feedbacks *not* including m; these are useful with the commonly-available 8-bit registers.

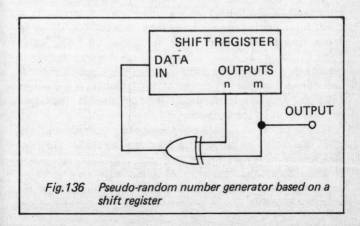

Fig.136   Pseudo-random number generator based on a shift register

14 Counters and dividers

Counters register the number of pulses received or, alternatively, are used as dividers. Counters of 1 to 3 stages are often conveniently built from D-type or JK flip-flops (Fig. 137). Those in the figure have 3 stages and therefore count up from 000 to 111 and then repeat; this gives 8 stages of counting. Conversely, the output of the third stage changes state at one-eighth the frequency of the input.

For longer counters, it is preferable to use an ic with these stages already connected. An example is the 7493 with 4 JK flip-flops. There is a single flip-flop, plus a chain of 3 (as in Fig.137(b)). In other words, it contains a divide-by-2 and a divide-by-8 divider. If the input is fed to the single flip-flop and the output of this goes to the chain, we have a 4-stage counter, with outputs running from 0000 to 1111 (decimal 15), and dividing by 16. The counter can be made to cycle with fewer counts by resetting it. Figure 138 shows the 7493 as a count-to-8 counter (divide-by-9 divider) resetting when the count reaches 1001. At this point, both reset inputs $R_0(_1)$ and $R_0(_2)$ are made high and the counter immediately resets to 0000. This technique is one of general application. Should the count to be detected have more than 2 high bits (e.g. a count of 1101), use a 3-input AND gate and feed its output to one reset input, the other reset input being wired to the positive supply.

The 7490 is similar to the 7493 but it is a decade counter containing a divide-by-2 and a divide-by-5 counter. It is used for counting from 0 to 9 by feeding the signal to input A and connecting output A to input B. The waveform of output D is not symmetrical, so this arrangement is unsuitable for frequency division. Feed the signal to input B and connect output D to input A. A symmetrical waveform (50% duty cycle) is obtained from output A. The same remarks apply to the 74390.

The counters so far described are known as *ripple counters* since the change of outputs ripples along the chain. They are also known as *asynchronous* counters. The important point is that during the change, the output may take spurious transition values. These values are short-lived and not noticeable, for example, if the counter is driving a digital display.

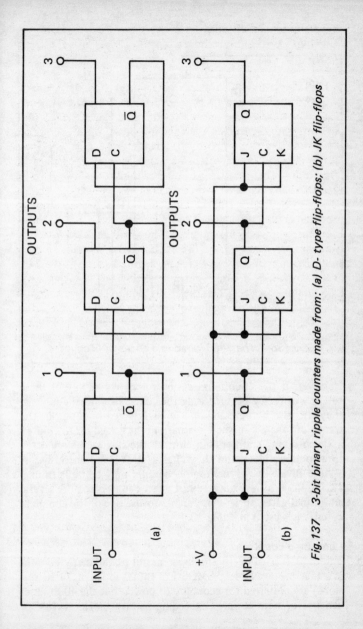

Fig. 137   3-bit binary ripple counters made from: (a) D- type flip-flops; (b) JK flip-flops

237

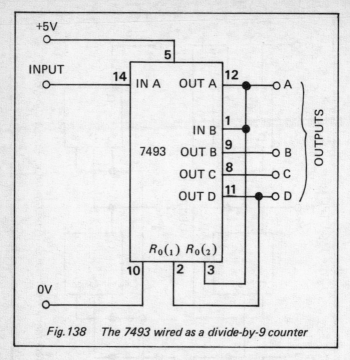

Fig.138   The 7493 wired as a divide-by-9 counter

However, if the circuit has gating for detecting any of these values when they occur during the course of normal counting, they will also be detected and possibly acted upon during the transition phase. In such a situation, the remedy is to employ a *synchronous* counter. In this, all the stages are connected to a common clock and they change state simultaneously. A 3-stage divide-by-8 synchronous counter may be built from 3 JK flip-flops, as in Figure 139. Longer counters require several additional gates, so it is preferable to use one of the complete counter ic's listed in Table 20.

Choosing a counter

Table 20 is a guide to the most useful of the many counter ic's that are available. CMOS ic's (4000 series or 74HC versions) are preferred for economy of power, but the 4000 series can not operate at rates exceeding about 10MHz at 10V or

238

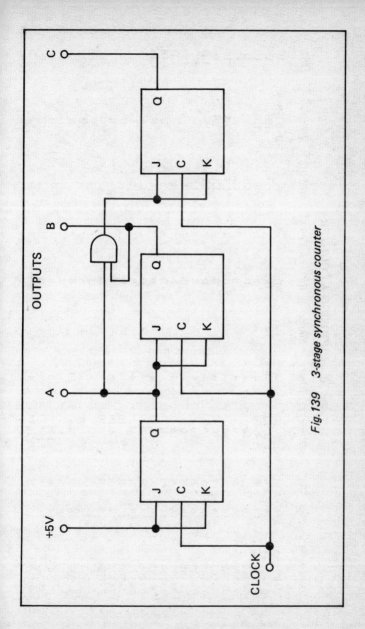

Fig. 139   3-stage synchronous counter

239

Table 20 – CHOOSING A COUNTER

Device No.	Pins	R/S	Divide by	Binary stages	Stages N/A	B/D	Clock	LOAD	RESET	U/D
7490	14	R	2, 5, 10	–	–	D	↓	–	HH=0 HH=9	U
7492	14	R	2, 6, 12	–	–	DD	↓	–	HH	U
7493	14	R	2, 8, 16	4	–	B	↓	–	HH	U
74160	16	S	10	–	–	D	↑	LS	L	U
74161	16	S	16	4	–	B	↑	LS	L	U
74162	16	S	10	–	–	D	↑	LS	LS	U
74163	16	S	16	4	–	B	↑	LS	LS	U
74168	16	S	10	–	–	D	↑	LS	–	UD
74169	16	S	16	4	–	B	↑	LS	–	UD
74190	16	S	10	–	–	D	↑	L	–	UD
74191	16	S	16	4	–	B	↑	L	–	UD
74192	16	S	10	–	–	D	↑	L	H	UDC
74193	16	S	16	4	–	B	↑	L	H	UDC
74196	14	R	2, 5	–	–	D	↓	L	L	U
74197	14	R	2, 8	4	–	B	↓	L	L	U
74390	16	R	10 × 10	–	–	D	↓	–	H	U
74393	14	R	16 × 16	8	–	B	↓	–	H	U
74HC490	16	R	10 × 10	–	–	D	↓	–	H=0 H=9	U
4017	16	S	10	–	–	J	↑	–	H	U
4018	16	S	2 to 10	–	2, 3	W	↑	–	H	U
4020	16	R	16384	14	–	B	↑	–	H	U
4022	16	S	8	–	–	J	↑	–	H	U
4024	14	R	128	7	–	B	↓	–	H	U
4026	16	S	10*	–	–	D	↑	–	H	U
4029	16	S	10/16**	4	–	B/D	↑	H	–	UD

Type	Pins	R/S	Divide by	Stages	Outputs	B/D	↑	LOAD	RESET	U/D
4033	16	S	10*	—	—	D	↑	—	H	U
4040	16	S	4096	12	—	B	↑	—	H	U
4045	16	R	2097152	21	1–20	B	—	—	—	U
4060+	16	R	16384	14	1–3,11	B	↑	—	H	U
40103	16	D	256	8	1–7	B	↑	H	H	D
40110	16	S	10*++	—	—	D	↑	—	H	UD
4510	16	S	10	4	—	D	↑	H	H	UD
4516	16	S	16	—	—	B	↑	H	H	UD
4518	16	S	10 × 10	—	—	D	↑	—	H	U
4520	16	S	16 × 16	8	1–17	B	↑	—	H	U
4521	16	S	16777216	24	—	B	↑	—	H	U
4522	16	D	10	4	—	D	↑	—	H	D
4526	16	D	16	—	—	B	↑	H	H	D

R/S: R = ripple counter; S = synchronous counter; D = down counter

Divide by: 10 × 10 and 16 × 16 indicate dual counters with division by 100 and by 256 respectively

Stages: the total number of binary stages in the counter; outputs can be taken from any stage except those listed in the next column B/D: B = Binary counter; D = decade counter; DD = duodecimal; J = Johnson counter with decoded outputs, one of which goes high in turn at each count (i.e. 'one-of-n' outputs); W = walking ring with decoding, programmable, intermediate stages not accessible

LOAD (or PRESET): L = low to load; H = high to load; S = synchronous loading

RESET (or CLEAR): L = low to reset; H = high to reset; L or H = one input; HH = two inputs, both H to reset; 0 = resets to 0 output; resets to 9 output; S = synchronous reset

U/D: up-down control input unless C specified, which means separate 'count up' and 'count down' clock inputs

* output decoded to drive 7-segment numeric display (see p.271)

** binary or decade counting selectable

+ has internal oscillator

++ latched outputs.

15V, or 5MHz at 5V. The 74HC series has very high rates, usually 40MHz or more. 74 and 74LS have higher power requirements but most can count at speeds of 30MHz or more.

Dividing crystal frequencies

Since all require many stages of binary division, one of the multi-stage CMOS counter/dividers is preferred. The 4060 has the advantage of having the oscillator circuit built-in. Here are some suggested circuits:

(i) **1Hz from 32.768kHz:** Requires division by 2^{15}. Use the 4060 with its built-in oscillator (Fig.140(a)), followed by a D-type flip-flop. Alternatively, use a pair of 4520 ic's, each with their two dividers cascaded. Tap the chain at stage 15 (Fig.140(b)).

(ii) **50Hz from 3.2768MHz:** Requires division by 2^{16}. Use two 4520 ic's to make a 16-stage chain as above, and take the output from pin 14 of IC2.

(iii) **1Hz from 4.194304MHz:** Requires division by 2^{22}. Use the 4521, tapped at stage 22.

15 Ramp and staircase generators

A number of circuits described in other parts of the book can be used as ramp generators. The UJT oscillator (p.155) produces a ramp at the positive terminal of the capacitor. This may be exponential but can be made linear by using a constant current generator. Given a small current and a relatively large capacitor, the ramp may last for several minutes. It is preferable to buffer the output with a voltage-follower op amp circuit (p.108) so that charging current is not lost to the following circuit. Another ramp generator, using an op amp, is described on page 110.

Using the ZN425E as a staircase ramp generator

The digital equivalent of a ramp may be produced by the ZN425E D-to-A converter (Fig.141). The output voltage ramps up from 0V in 256 steps. The output has 10kΩ output impedance so it is best to buffer it. Use an op amp wired either as a voltage follower (p.108) or as a non-inverting amplifier (p.105). With amplification, the circuit can be made to

242

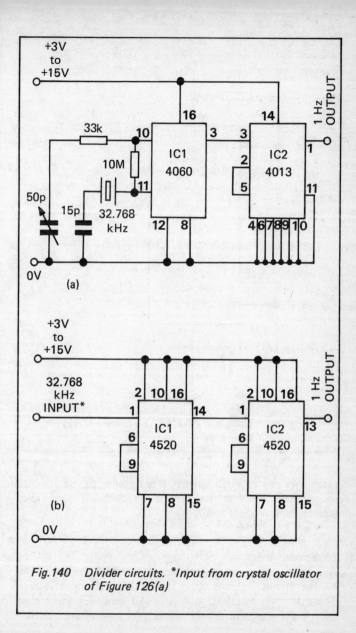

Fig. 140   Divider circuits. *Input from crystal oscillator
of Figure 126(a)

243

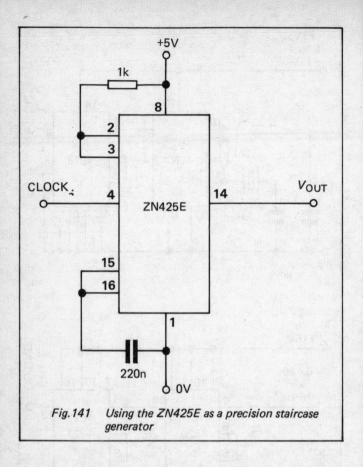

Fig.141   Using the ZN425E as a precision staircase generator

ramp over any required range. Offset nulling can be provided to give exactly 0V at the start of the ramp. The period of ramping in seconds is $256/f_{CLK}$.

16 Schmitt triggers

A Schmitt trigger is a bistable circuit in which the state taken by the circuit depends upon the level of the input voltage. There are two *threshold voltages*. An increasing input must exceed the *upper threshold* before a change of state occurs.

The return to the previous stage does not occur until the input falls below the *lower threshold*. The difference in level between the two thresholds is the *hysteresis* (or *dead band*) of the trigger. Schmitt triggers are important for interfacing analogue inputs to digital circuits. They produce a sharp change of state, with a clear swing from logic low to logic high (or *vice versa*), even though the analogue input may be changing slowly and erratically, or there is a large amount of noise on it.

Logic devices with Schmitt inputs

Several logic ic's have Schmitt inputs, thus making it possible to combine interfacing with the analogue world with the first stage of logical processing. Choose from the devices listed in Table 21.

Transistor trigger circuit

A basic 2-transistor trigger circuit appears in Figure 142. This can drive a load such as a filament lamp, an LED with series resistor, or a relay coil. If a resistor is substituted for the load, the output (shown by the dotted line) is TTL or CMOS compatible.

Unless threshold levels and hysteresis are critical, suitable values are R_L = 470Ω, R_C = 1kΩ (for this circuit to operate, R_C *must* be greater than R_L), and R_E = 56Ω. For greater hysteresis, increase the value of R_E to possibly as much as 1kΩ. Hysteresis can also be set by altering the ratio between R_L and R_C and also the ratio of the resistors of the potential divider from the collector of TR1 to ground. If higher input impedance is essential, replace TR1 with an FET such as a 2N3819.

CMOS Schmitt trigger

Two CMOS inverter gates, which may be inverting buffer gates, or NAND or NOR gates with their inputs wired together, may be used to build a simple Schmitt circuit (Fig. 143). If V is the supply voltage, the threshold points are given by:

$$V_H = \frac{V}{2} \left(1 + \frac{R1}{R2} \right)$$

245

Table 21 – LOGIC DEVICES WITH SCHMITT INPUTS

Device No.	Gate function	Thresholds at supply voltages					
		5V		10V		15V	
		Lower	Upper	Lower	Upper	Lower	Upper
7413	Dual 4-input NAND	0.9	1.7	–	–	–	–
74LS13		0.8	1.6	–	–	–	–
7414	Hex inverter	0.9	1.7	–	–	–	–
74LS14		0.8	1.6	–	–	–	–
74HC14		1.7	2.8	–	–	–	–
74132	Quad 2-input NAND	0.9	1.7	–	–	–	–
74LS132		0.8	1.6	–	–	–	–
74HC132		1.7	2.9	–	–	–	–
4093	Quad 2-input NAND	2.4	2.7	4.1	4.4	5.5	6.0
40106	Hex inverter	1.9	2.9	3.9	5.9	5.8	8.9
4584	Hex inverter (OD)	2.3	2.9	3.9	5.9	–	–

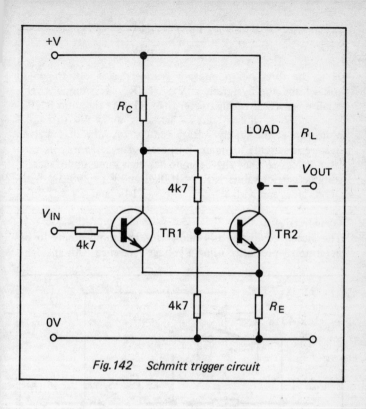

Fig.142   Schmitt trigger circuit

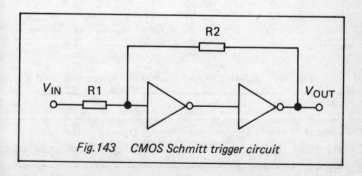

Fig.143   CMOS Schmitt trigger circuit

247

and
$$V_L = \frac{V}{2} \left(1 - \frac{R1}{R2}\right)$$

Thus the threshold points are symmetrical about the mid-voltage and the hysteresis is $V \times R1/R2$. Hysteresis is very small when R2 is much greater than R1. As the ratio R1/R2 approaches 1, the hysteresis increases until the threshold points are at the supply voltage and 0V. A ratio of 1:4 gives hysteresis suitable for many purposes. The resistors can have large values so that the Schmitt has high input impedance; a suitable pair of values is R1 = 100kΩ and R2 = 390kΩ. With these values and with V = 5V V_H = 3.14V and V_L = 1.86V.

Op amp trigger

The circuit of Figure 144 allows the threshold points to be determined precisely, using a voltage reference. An analogue

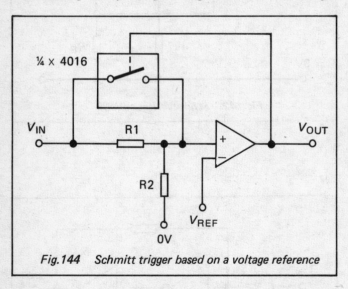

Fig.144 *Schmitt trigger based on a voltage reference*

switch (possibly from a 4016, though one with lower on-resistance would improve performance) is used to short-circuit R1 when the output of the Schmitt is high. The thresholds are:

248

$$V_H = V_{REF} \times \frac{R1 + R2}{R2}$$

$$V_L = V_{REF}$$

Thus the hysteresis is $V_{REF} \times$ R1/R2. R1 must be large in comparison with the on-resistance of the switch.

17 Digital-to-analogue converters

Simple D-to-A converter

This circuit (Fig.145) converts a 4-bit input but can be extended to more digits if required. It operates on the same principle as the op amp mixer (p.109). The four buffers are not necessary if inputs are available direct from identical logic outputs. The current from the buffers is weighted by resistors. The least significant data bit has the highest resistor. If more than 4 bits are required, begin the series with D_0 as a smaller resistor, so that there is a $1k\Omega$ resistor for the most significant bit.

The output voltage is 0V for a zero input and falls with increasing digital input. If the feedback resistor is 470Ω, the full-scale voltage is $-0.88 \times V_{SUPPLY}$. A variable resistor may be used in series with the feedback resistor to allow the full-scale voltage to be set to a convenient value.

The ZN425E D-to-A converter

Figure 146 gives the basic circuit for this 8-bit converter. It requires a regulated 5V supply and its inputs are compatible with TTL and CMOS. Supply current is 30mA. The output ranges between 0V for an all-zero input to 2.55V for an all-high input (1111 1111, equivalent to 255 decimal). Thus the output is 10mV per unit on the binary scale. The output impedance is $10k\Omega$ so needs to be buffered with a voltage follower (p.108) if appreciable current is required. The output is subject to an offset voltage error of 3mV (typically) when all inputs are zero. For many purposes this can be ignored, but it can be compensated for by feeding the output to an op

249

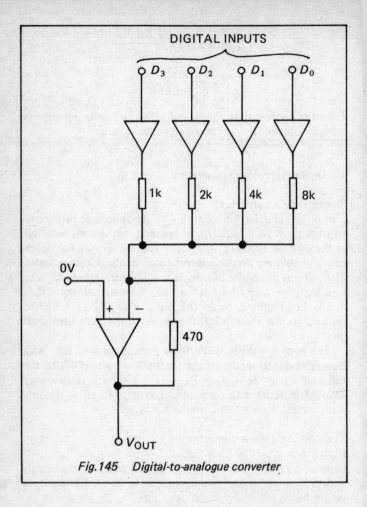

Fig.145   Digital-to-analogue converter

amp connected as a non-inverting amplifier. The input offset adjustment of the amplifier is used as a zero adjustment. If an op amp is used it can also incorporate variable gain to set the full-scale output voltage to any desired value. Note that the full-scale should occur when input is 256, but the maximum input is only 255. Therefore, for greatest precision, the gain should be set to give 255/256 of full scale when the inputs

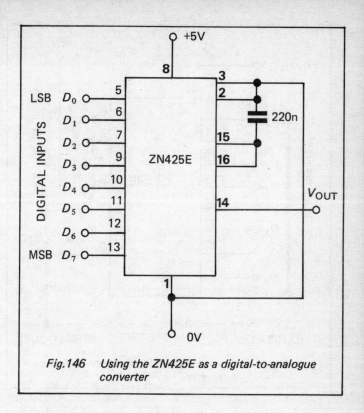

Fig.146   Using the ZN425E as a digital-to-analogue
converter

are all high.

This ic is also used in an analogue-to-digital circuit (p.255)
and in a staircase generator (p.242).

The ZN428E digital-to-analogue converter

This ic is similar to the ZN425E, but has latches on the digital
input. When the ENABLE input is low (Fig.147), the data
passes straight to the conversion circuit and the corresponding
analogue voltage appears at the output, changing as the data
changes. When ENABLE goes high, the data is held in latches.
The latched data is converted and V_{OUT} remains constant at
the converted value until ENABLE goes low again. This
feature is useful for sampling digital data at a given instant.

251

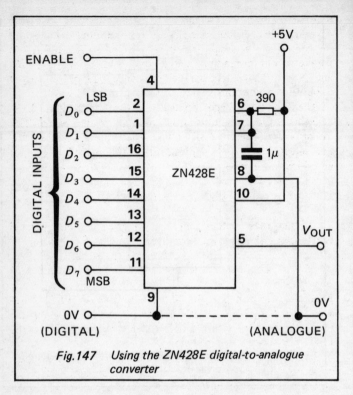

Fig.147   Using the ZN428E digital-to-analogue converter

If successive data samples are to be read on a meter, it is useful to be able to latch the output long enough for the meter reading to be taken.

The ic has separate analogue and digital ground terminals. This allows separate ground lines to be used to prevent noise passing from one side to the other. The two grounds may differ by as much as 200mV without interfering with the action of the converter. If more convenient, both terminals may be connected to a common ground line, as indicated by the dashed connection.

The output impedance of the analogue output is 4kΩ. It can be buffered by an op amp if appreciable current is to be drawn. The op amp should have an input bias current less than 1.5µA; use one with JFET or CMOS inputs. The op amp may be connected as a non-inverting amplifier, as in Figure 47(a) (p.106), except that R_B is not required. The input impedance of the amplifier circuit is equal to R_F and R_A in parallel. For minimum thermal drift, choose values of R_F and R_A so that their parallel resistance equals the output impedance of the converter, i.e. 4kΩ.

The internal voltage reference of the converter is 2.5V, and this is the maximum output voltage for an input of 256. To obtain a different FSD voltage, the values of R_F and R_A are selected so as to produce the appropriate degree of amplification A, where:

$$A = V_{FS}/V_{REF} = (R_F + R_A)/R_A$$

To obtain these values and also to give the total parallel resistance of 4kΩ, use the formulae:

$$R_F = 4A \quad \text{and} \quad R_A = 4A/(A-1) \quad \text{(both in kΩ)}$$

Example: the gain is to be A = 1.6 to give 4V FSD. R_F = 1.6 × 4 = 6.4kΩ. R_A = 10.7kΩ. R_A can be a fixed resistor of 8.2kΩ in series with a 4.7kΩ variable resistor to allow the FSD to be set exactly (see below).

To set up the circuit, first provide an all-low digital input, corresponding to V_{OUT} = 0V. If using an op amp with offset null adjustment, set output to 0V. Now provide an all-high input. This is 255 in decimal so the expected output is 255/256 of FSD. Use the variable resistor to set V_{OUT} accordingly.

This ic can be used in a number of other circuits, for details of which the reader is referred to the manufacturer's data and applications sheets.

18 Analogue-to-digital converters

Using a D-to-A converter as an A-to-D converter

A simple A-to-D converter may be built from a D-to-A converter, a counter, an op amp and a timer ic (Fig.148). The D-to-A converter could be any type that does not

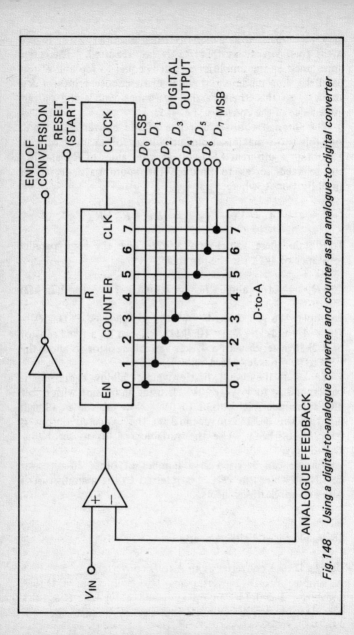

Fig.148   Using a digital-to-analogue converter and counter as an analogue-to-digital converter

incorporate its own counter. The timer is used as a clock running at, say, 1kHz. The exact rate does not matter, the main point being that it may take up to 255 counts to perform the conversion. The pulse train from the clock (which could be a 555 timer, p.226) is fed to an 8-stage counter. The 4020 is a suitable counter (p.240). It does not have the output from stages 2 and 3 available, but the outputs 4 to 11 can be used instead. The clock frequency can be increased fourfold to keep the conversion time short.

Conversion is started by a low pulse on the reset line. This clears the counter. Its all-low digital output is converted to a zero volt output by the converter. The op amp compares this with the analogue voltage V_{IN}. This is normally higher than 0V, so the output of the op amp swings high, enabling the counter. The counter increases steadily and as it does so the output from the converter increases in proportion. Eventually this voltage *just* exceeds V_{IN}. The op amp output swings low, disabling the counter. The count which is then held on it, and which can be read on the digital outputs D0 to D7, is the equivalent of V_{IN}. The output of the inverter gate goes low to indicate 'end of conversion'.

Using the ZN425E as an A-to-D converter

The ZN425E has its own counter, not used when the ic is functioning as a D-to-A converter, but intended to allow it to function for A-to-D conversion. The principle is the same as that outlined in the previous section, a little extra logic being required (Fig.149). A low-going start pulse resets the counter in the ZN425E and also resets the flip-flop formed by the two cross-connected NAND gates. The output of the flip-flop goes high, allowing clock pulses to pass to the counter, and also makes the end of conversion (EOC) output go high. The op amp compares V_{IN} with the analogue output of the converter as in the description above. When conversion is complete, the op amp sets the flip-flop, no further clock pulses pass to the counter, EOC goes high, and the converted output appears on the digital outputs.

The ZN427E A-to-D converter

This has a maximum conversion time of 15μs. It has 3-state outputs, so is suitable for connecting to a data bus. It accepts

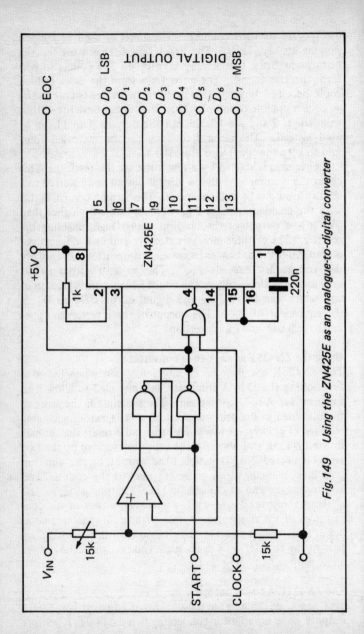

Fig.149 Using the ZN425E as an analogue-to-digital converter

256

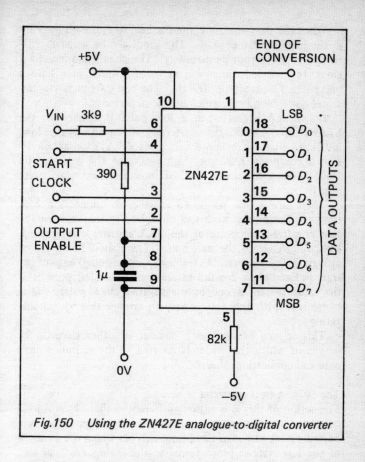

Fig.150 Using the ZN427E analogue-to-digital converter

an analogue voltage in the range 0V to 2.5V (the internal reference voltage) converting to the corresponding digital output in the range 0000 0000 to 1111 1111. The positive supply voltage is +5V. It also requires a negative supply in the range −3V to −30V. Figure 150 shows an 82kΩ resistor being used with a −5V supply; this value is calculated so as to provide a current I_{EXT} which must be between 25μA and 150μA. The current required is so small that, if this is the only requirement for a negative supply, it can be provided by a 7660 voltage converter (p.86).

257

When the output enable input is held low, the outputs are in the high-impedance state. This input can be wired to +5V to enable the output permanently. The circuit is driven by a clock (e.g. a 555 timer circuit, p.226), which may have a maximum frequency of 900kHz. The clock frequency determines conversion time, which is 9 clock periods.

Conversion begins when a low pulse is applied to the START input. At this time EOC (end of conversion) goes low, indicating that conversion is taking place. As soon as conversion is complete, EOC goes high again and the data may be read. The data remains latched until the next start pulse occurs.

There are a few points to consider in connection with timing. There must be a gap of at least $1.5\mu s$ between the first negative-going pulse of the clock and the leading (negative-going) edge of the start pulse. There should be a gap of at least 200ns between the trailing (positive-going) edge of the start pulse. These conditions are met if the start pulse is of the same length as one of the negative clock pulses and is coincident with this. It is easy to arrange this by suitable gating logic.

This ic can be used in a number of other circuits, for details of which the reader is referred to the manufacturer's data and applications sheets.

The 507C A-to-D converter

The action of this ic is entirely different to that of the A-to-D converter described above. It converts an analogue input to a pulsed digital output of fixed frequency, in which the duration of the low state is proportional to the analogue voltage (see Fig.151).

The ic operates on either an unregulated supply of 8V to 18V or a regulated supply of 3.5V to 6V (fed to pin 6). A regulated supply is connected to pin 6 and pin 7 is left unconnected. An unregulated supply is connected to pin 7 and in this case a reference voltage can be obtained at pin 6; this gives a voltage of 5.6V (typically, though it can range from 5V to 6V) and supply up to 1mA.

The reset pin is held low (0) when the ic is running. If the output enable pin is low, output is high. As soon as the output

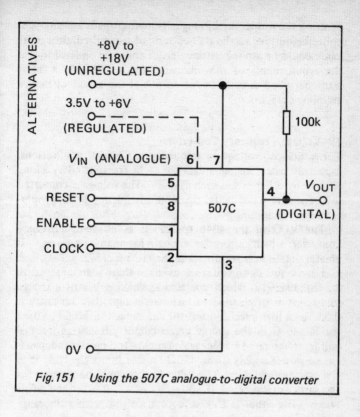

Fig. 151   Using the 507C analogue-to-digital converter

enable is made high, and provided that V_{IN} is greater than the minimum value of 200mV, the output can begin to deliver its stream of pulses. The width of the pulses depends upon a ramp voltage that is internally generated. Given a regulated supply voltage of 5V, V_{RAMP} falls from 3.75V to 1.25V in each cycle of operation. While V_{RAMP} is higher than V_{IN} the output is high but, as soon as V_{RAMP} falls below V_{IN}, the output falls low. Thus, the higher the level of V_{IN}, the sooner V_{RAMP} falls below it on each cycle and the shorter the high pulse period.

The ramp voltage range is determined by the supply voltage, V_{CC}, ramping down from $0.755 V_{CC}$ to $0.25 V_{CC}$. By using an appropriate supply voltage, the ramp voltage can be made to cover a different range. Note that the ic has an open-collector output, so the pull-up resistor is required, though its value could be altered or the resistor could be omitted to suit the requirements of the following circuit. The clock input must be wired directly to the output of the clock, without a coupling capacitor.

19 Voltage/Frequency Converters
Conversion of voltage to frequency has several applications, especially when analogue data has to be transmitted by a long wire or by other means such as radio. The voltage is converted into a square wave digital signal, the frequency being proportional to voltage.

The VCO of the 4046 (p.222) is a voltage-to-frequency converter which is precise enough for many purposes. If greater precision is required, use the 8038 (p.157).

For frequency-to-voltage conversion there is an inexpensive ic, the LM2917, which operates by making use of a charge pump. It is often used in tachometer circuits. Linearity is 0.3%, so a high-precision resistor and capacitor should be used for R and C in the charge pump circuit. It has an internal voltage reference (7.56V) which makes the output independent of power supply. The 470Ω resistor limits the current to the voltage reference. The value of this could be increased if the device is operated at voltages toward the top end of its range. The input is able to accept a signal within the range ±28V. The output signal is given by:

$$V_{OUT} = F_{IN} \times 7.56RC$$

The maximum V_{OUT} obtainable is 6.4V, so R and C are limited to values which give this maximum at the maximum frequency that is to be measured. This table suggests suitable values for R and C:

Maximum frequency (Hz)	C (nF)	R (kΩ)
10	100	820
100	10	820
1000	10	82

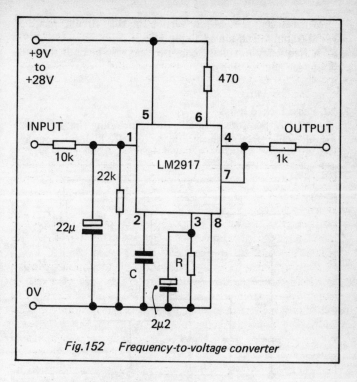

Fig.152   Frequency-to-voltage converter

These give a maximum output of 6.2V.

The pin numbers shown in Figure 152 apply to the 8-pin version of this ic. There is also a 14-pin version, and the corresponding pin numbers are:

8-pin	14-pin
1	1
2	2
3	3/4
4	5
5	8
6	9
7	10
8	11/12

When using the 14-pin version in this circuit, pin 3 is wired to pin 4, and pin 11 to pin 12.

A frequency-to-voltage converter can also be built from the 4046 (see next section).

20 Phase locked loops

The NE567 has several applications, including that of a tone decoder (Fig.153). The output is normally high but goes low

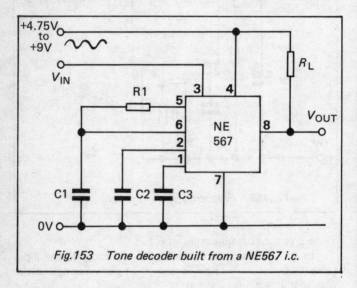

Fig.153 Tone decoder built from a NE567 i.c.

when a signal within the given range of frequency is detected. V_{IN} is the signal input; the minimum amplitude signal for detection is 20mV (rms). The recommended maximum amplitude is 200mV (rms). The centre frequency f_0 is determined by the timing resistor R1 and the timing capacitor C1. R1 must have a value between 2kΩ and 20kΩ. The formula for the centre frequency is:

$$f_0 = \frac{1.1}{R1 \times C1}$$

The bandwidth is determined by signal amplitude and the value of the loop filter capacitor C2. If BW is the bandwidth as a percentage of f_0, then:

$$BW = 1070\sqrt{V_{IN}/(f_0 \times C2)}$$

where C2 is expressed in microfarads. Bandwidth can be up to 14% of f_0. If the signal frequency falls within this band, the ic locks on to it and output goes low. Note that the output is an open-collector transistor and so requires a pull-up resistor, R_L. The ic may also lock on to the harmonic frequencies $5f_0$, $9f_0$, $13f_0$, etc., so, if these frequencies are likely to be present, the signal must be passed through a low-pass filter to remove them. The value of the output filter capacitor C3 is not critical; usually a value twice that of C2 is suitable.

Example: design a tone decoder to detect a signal of 10 kHz, bandwidth 10%, with a signal of rms amplitude 100mV.

$$R1 \times C1 = 1.1/(10 \times 10^3) = 1.1 \times 10^{-4}$$

Given that R1 = 11kΩ, then C1 = $(1.1 \times 10^{-4})/(11 \times 10^3)$ = 10nF. The bandwidth formula above is rearranged to give:

$$C2 = \frac{1070^2 \times V_{IN}}{BW^2 \times f_0} = \frac{1070^2 \times 100 \times 10^{-3}}{10^2 \times 10 \times 10^3} = 0.11\mu F$$

A 100nF capacitor is a standard value, which would give a slightly wider bandwidth. C3 could be 200nF.

The CMOS 4046 ic is an adaptable device for PLL applications. The action of the VCO is described on page 223. When connected in a PLL, as in Figure 154, the VCO is made to lock on to signals within its frequency range. In calculating the values of the timing resistors and capacitor, it is essential for the frequency range to cover, or slightly more than cover, the expected frequency range of the input signal. The maximum frequency ranges from 0.8MHz at 5V to 2.4MHz at 15V.

The figure shows an optional divider in the loop and this affects the operation of the circuit. If a divide-by-n frequency

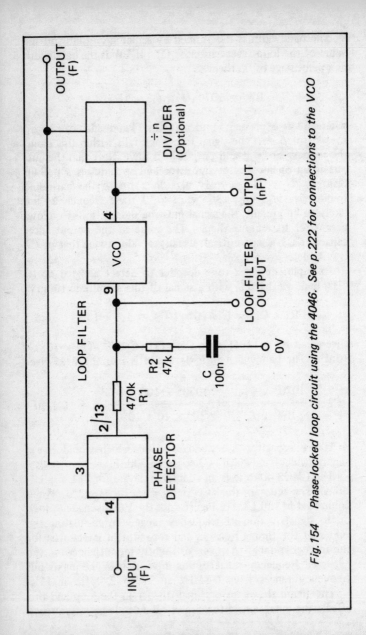

Fig. 154 Phase-locked loop circuit using the 4046. See p.222 for connections to the VCO

divider is in the loop, the VCO produces an output (at pin 4) which has n times the frequency of the input. This makes the PLL useful as a frequency multiplier. The output from the divider has the same frequency as the input signal. The outputs from both the VCO and the divider are likely to be an improvement on the input as they are properly squared-off waves, swinging fully and cleanly from logic low to logic high, whereas the input signal may be one that is severely distorted, and possibly variable in amplitude. The cleaning up of signals or the 'extraction' of them from background noise is another application of PLLs. If the divider is not required, simply connect pin 4 directly to pin 3.

The 4046 has two phase detectors, which have contrasting properties:

Wideband: Output from pin 13. When this is used, the VCO can track frequencies within a wide range (1:1000) and the duty cycle of the input signal can be far from 50%. The output is in phase with the input. The loop is insensitive to harmonics. Noise rejection is poor. In the absence of a signal the VCO frequency falls to the bottom end of its range.

Low-noise: Output at pin 2. This tracks signals over a narrower range (±30%), and requires the signal to be a square wave with 50% duty cycle. It is highly immune to noise on the input signal. The output is 90° out of phase when the input is f_0. The loop is very sensitive to harmonics. In the absence of a signal the VCO goes to f_0.

Input to the phase detector can be direct or capacitor coupled. The input is sensitive to an a.c. signal of a 200mV peak-to-peak at 5V, 700mV at 15V. With capacitor coupling a suitable value is 1nF; it is advisable to connect a 10kΩ resistor between pin 14 and 0V.

Figure 154 suggests values for the resistors and capacitor of the loop filter. These are good starting values but improved performance may be obtained if these values are amended. Appropriate values can be calculated by techniques which are outside the scope of this book. Alternatively, values can be obtained by trial and error. The two points to consider are:

(1) R1 and C determine the settling time of the loop, i.e. how long it takes to settle after a change of frequency. The

action depends upon the time constant RC. If RC is too large, settling time is increased and the loop may not be able to follow rapid changes in frequency. If RC is too small, it settles so quickly that it fails to lock on properly and the VCO frequency fluctuates wildly.

(2) The ratio between R1 and R2 determines the damping of the loop. If R1/R2 is too large, the loop becomes unstable; it may even start to oscillate. If R1/R2 is too small, the loop does not adjust quickly to changes in frequency.

The loop filter output is a voltage which indicates how the circuit is currently reacting to the input signal. To avoid draining current from the capacitor, this output should be fed to a voltage follower (p.108). When using the wideband phase detector, the loop filter output varies as in this table:

Input frequency	Loop filter output
Below range of VCO	logic low (0V)
Within range of VCO	Between 0V and V_{SS}
Above range of VCO	logic high (V_{SS})

Provided that the input frequency is within the range of the VCO, the circuit acts as a frequency-to-voltage converter.

21 Light emitting diode displays

Light emitting diodes
Typical LEDs have the following properties:

Colour: red (peak at 635nm)
Viewing angle: $\pm 20°$ to $\pm 60°$
Usual operating forward current I_F = 10mA
Maximum forward current I_{MAX} = 40mA
Light intensity at I_F = 1 to 6 mcd (most are 4 to 5 mcd)
Forward voltage drop V_F (at I_F) = 2V
Maximum reverse voltage V_R = 5V

The low value of V_R for LEDs compared with most other diodes except Zeners is an important practical consideration. LEDs that are connected with the wrong polarity may be rapidly destroyed by the reverse voltage. Several types of LED have V_R as low as 3V.

LEDs are available in a range of colours: red, red-orange, orange, yellow and green. Yellow and green LEDs are less efficient and are usually run with I_F of 20mA.

Brightness is specified in millicandela (mcd) for a given I_F. When a number of separate LEDs are to be assembled into an array, it is important to buy the slightly more expensive types that are guaranteed matched for brightness.

LEDs of higher than standard efficiency fall into three categories:

Low current LEDs: combine moderate brightness (about 2mcd) with low current requirements (2–3mA) and are recommended for battery-powered projects which are to be left switched on for hours at a time.

Extra-bright LEDs: range in brightness up to about 250 mcd. They may require up to 30mA to achieve this. The terminology of manufacturers and retailers is not consistent when describing brightness; 'high intensity', 'super-bright' and 'ultra-bright' are relative terms with no absolute meaning. The only way to be certain about brightness is to refer to the data tables in the catalogue, quoting the brightness in millicandela.

Gallium aluminium arsenide (GaAlAs) LEDs: have intensities up to 3cd for a relatively low (20mA) current, though this may be partly at the expense of a narrow viewing angle ($\pm 10°$).

Constant current LEDs include a current-regulating circuit, so remain at constant brightness over a wide range of supply voltage (e.g. 5V–15V). A series resistor is not required.

Bi-colour and tri-colour LEDs consist of two LEDs in the same package. In bi-colour LEDs the two (red/green or yellow/green) are connected in parallel but in the opposite sense. Depending on the direction of the applied voltage one or the other comes on. These are useful for indicating polarity or for other 'true/false' binary indications. In tri-colour LEDs the two diodes (red/green) are connected with the same polarity and a common cathode terminal so that both can be lit at the same time. With both lit at once the resulting colour is yellow. Intermediate tints are produced by controlling the relative brightness of the LEDs.

Flashing LEDs are useful for generating alarm signals without the need for building an astable. The astable is included and typically flashes the LED at 2Hz. These LEDs operate on a wide supply range (often 4–15V) and do not need a series resistor.

Series resistor

Unless the supply voltage is 2V or the LED is a flashing or constant current type, an LED requires a resistor in series with it to limit the current to a safe level (Fig.155(a)). The formula for calculating the resistor value is:

$$R_S = \frac{V_{SUPPLY} - V_F}{I_F}$$

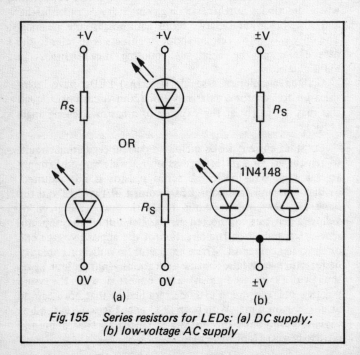

Fig.155   Series resistors for LEDs: (a) DC supply;
(b) low-voltage AC supply

Typically $V_F = 2$ and $I_F = 10$mA, so the formula becomes:

$$R_S = 100(V_{SUPPLY} - 2)$$

For the commonly used supply voltages and $I_F = 10$mA, the required resistors in the E12 range are:

V_{SUPPLY}	R_S (Ω)
4.5	270
5	270 or 330
6	390
9	680
12	1000
15	1200

Use half these values for $I_F = 20$mA, or when powering the LED from low-voltage AC, as in Figure 155(b).

Driving individual LEDs

LEDs can be driven directly from analogue outputs, but unless the output has ample current to spare, the LED is better driven by using a transistor in the saturated mode (Fig.156(a)). The value of R_S is calculated as above. The LED comes on when V_{IN} exceeds a certain level. If the circuit is such that V_{IN} hovers around the switch-on level, the action may be made more definite by using a Schmitt trigger circuit (p.244). If only a small current is available, replace the single transistor of Figure 156(a) with a Darlington pair (p.35), and increase the value of the base resistor.

The transistor switch may also be used with CMOS outputs which do not provide sufficient current to drive an LED directly (except a low-current LED when the supply voltage is 15V). If several LEDs are to be driven from separate CMOS outputs, use the μA75491PC ic which has four Darlington pairs and associated resistors, specially intended for interfacing CMOS to LEDs.

Figure 156(b)–(c) show how to drive LEDs from TTL outputs, or from CMOS buffers (e.g. 4049, 4050). If buffers are used, these can be inverting or non-inverting types, depending on whether the LED is to be on for low or for high inputs.

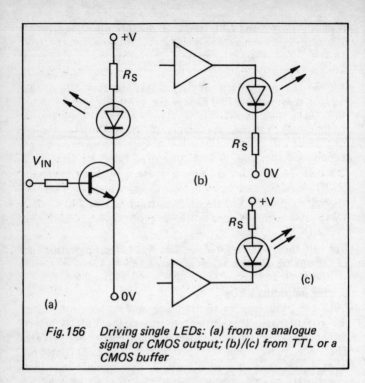

Fig. 156 Driving single LEDs: (a) from an analogue signal or CMOS output; (b)/(c) from TTL or a CMOS buffer

When calculating R_S and when deciding if fanout to other gates is possible, refer to the tables on pages 187 to 189.

In Figure 156(b), the LED is on when the gate output is high. The current available is I_{OH}. The table shows that only the 74AC at 4.5V or more provide sufficient current to illuminate an LED at all brightly. With the other families, and provided that low brightness is acceptable, use the circuit of Figure 156(b), omitting R_S. There will be no current to spare for fanout to other gates. If fanout is essential, the LED must be driven by a separate (preferably buffer) gate. If brightness is essential, use a transistor switch (Fig.156(a)) or a buffer gate.

With the 74AC series, the gate can provide 24mA, all of which is available to drive the LED, or which can be shared between the LED and fanout to other gates. For maximum

270

brightness drive the LED only; no resistor being needed. If the supply voltage is 5V and 10mA is taken for the LED (R_S = 330Ω, see table on page 269), this leaves 14mA for fanout, which is enough to supply a large number of CMOS gates).

In Figure 156(c), the LED is on when the gate output is low. The current available is I_{OL}. The table shows that outputs of all series can supply sufficient current, though brightness will be minimal with CMOS gates operated on a 5V supply and there will be no current to spare for fanout. A standard 74 series output provides 10mA for the LED (R_S = 330Ω), leaving 6mA for up to four 74 series inputs.

Buffers provide additional current for driving LEDs. This table lists commonly used buffers (6 per ic) and typical output currents, in milliamps:

Inverting/	74		74LS	CMOS
Non-inverting	7406*	7416+	366/368	4049
	7407*	7417+	365	4050
I_{OH}	−0.25	−0.25	−2.6	−2.5 @ 5V
				−2.6 @ 10V
				−10 @ 15V
I_{OL}	40	40	24	6 @ 5V
				16 @ 10V
				40 @ 15V

* open-collector outputs; can be connected to +30V max.
+ open-collector outputs; can be connected to +15V max.

A flashing LED attracts more attention than one that is continuously lit. Flashing LEDs are intended for this purpose but ordinary LEDs can be flashed by driving them from the output of an astable circuit. A special ic for flashing LEDs is the LM3909 (p.216).

7-segment LED displays

The 7-segment display, which usually also includes one or two decimal points, has its segments specified by letters *a* to *g*

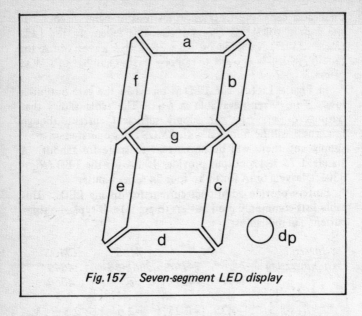

Fig.157   Seven-segment LED display

according to a standard scheme (Fig.157). The pin-outs vary
according to the type and manufacturer. Displays are available with 1, 2 or more digits, each independently accessible.
Apart from various sizes and styles, there are two main
kinds of display:

Common anode: the anodes of all segments are connected
to a single pin, sometimes all to two pins.

Common cathode: as above but with cathodes so connected. It is essential to use the correct kind with any given
display driving circuit. The LEDs usually have similar
characteristics to single LEDs and the calculation of R_S for
each segment is as described above.

7-segment display drivers

It is usual to employ an ic which has all the logic for accepting
a 4-bit binary-coded decimal input and decoding it so that the
output lights the coded segments of the display.

The 7447 is illustrated in Figure 158. The ic can be used to
drive a single display but here we show two ic's driving two

272

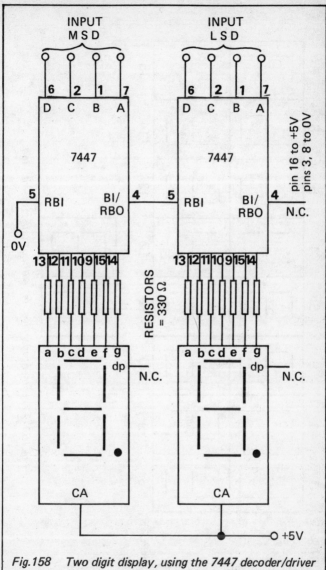

Fig. 158   Two digit display, using the 7447 decoder/driver

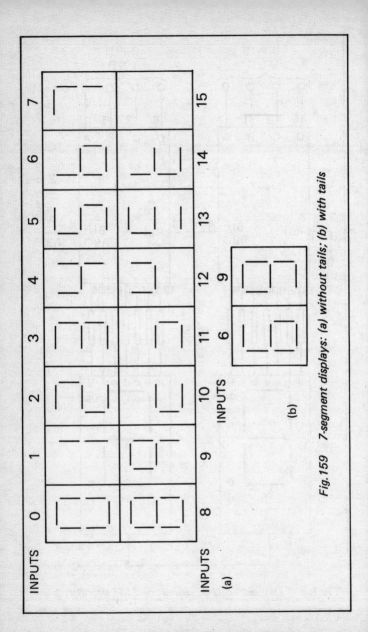

Fig.159 7-segment displays: (a) without tails; (b) with tails

274

displays to represent the 'units' digit (LSD) and 'tens' digit (MSD) to illustrate the principles involved in a multi-digit display. The input to each ic is a 4-bit binary number. The 7447 has open-collector outputs which are *active-low*. The outputs go low which correspond to the segments that are to be lit. The situation for each digit is as in Figure 156(c), so a *common anode* display is needed. Figure 159(a) shows how the display lights for each input combination, including the 'illegal' combinations representing 10 to 15.

The ripple blanking input (RBI) controls the action of the ic when input is zero (0000). With RBI high, a zero is produced as in Figure 159(a) but, with RBI low the display goes blank. This provides for leading zero blanking, so that the display shows '7' for example, instead of '07'. For a display of more digits the rule is: connect RBI of the MSD to 0V. Connect the BI/RBO output of each ic to the next ic along to the right. Leave the BI/RBO of the LSD unconnected.

In Figure 158, pin 3 is listed as connected to 0V. This is the lamp test pin and, if this pin is made high, all segments are turned on.

The ic allows for trailing zero blanking for a display with digits below the decimal point, though this is less often required. Connect RBI of the right-hand (LSD) ic to 0V, connect the BI/RBO output of each ic to the RBI input of the ic to its left. Leave the left-most ic (just below the decimal point) with its BI/RBO output unconnected.

The 7447 is also available in the 74LS series and there are several related ic's available only in 74LS form:

74LS48 has internal pull-up resistors ($2k\Omega$) and is active-high (use a common cathode display);

74LS49 is a 14-pin ic, with open-collector active-high outputs (use a common cathode display); it has no lamp-test or ripple blanking inputs.

The 74LS247, 74LS248 and 74LS249 are identical with the three ic's described above except that they produce 6 and 9 with tails (Fig.159(b)).

Of the CMOS ic's, the 4511 is the most popular (Fig.160). It differs from the 7447 in several ways.

The display goes blank for all inputs 10 to 15.

It requires a common *cathode* display unit.

275

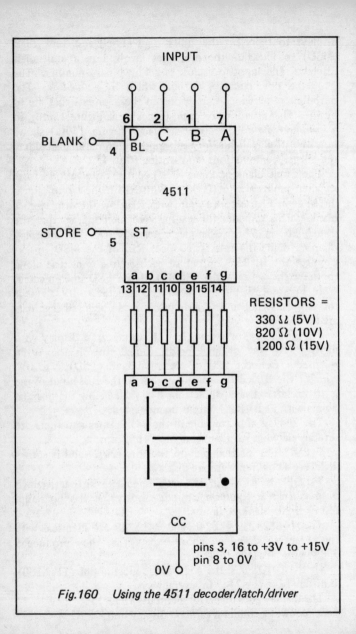

Fig.160   Using the 4511 decoder/latch/driver

276

It has a STORE input; low, output follows input; high output is latched.

There are no inputs for ripple-blanking.

The blank input blanks the display when it is made low; this may be used to control brightness by feeding it with a pulsed input of variable duty cycle. The lamp test input (pin 3) turns all segments on when it is made low.

Another class of display driver is illustrated by the 4033 decade counter/driver (Fig.161). This produces 6 and 9 with tails, as in Figure 159(b). It has a single CLOCK input which advances the counter on the positive-going edge, provided that CLOCK ENABLE is high. Counting is ignored if CE is low. The RESET input is normally held low. Segment outputs are active-high, so a common cathode display is required.

The ic's may be cascaded by connecting the 'divide by 10' output to the clock input of the next more significant digit. This display goes low at counts 5 to 9, and goes high at count 0 to 4, incrementing the next counter at the 9–0 transition. The ic's have ripple-blanking, which is connected as in Figure 159. If this is not required, connect all RBI pins to the positive rail.

The LAMP TEST input (pin 14) is normally held low. The 4033 may be used for driving LCDs, but external AC drive must be provided.

LED displays can also be driven by the 4056 and 4543 (p.282).

LED bargraph display

Figure 162 shows the connections for the LM3914 bargraph driver. The ic accepts an input V_{IN} in the range 0V to 1.5V below the supply voltage. The input voltage is compared with a number of voltages produced by a chain of resistors inside the ic. The resistor chain runs from pin 6 (R_{HI}) to pin 4 (R_{LO}). The ends of the chain may be connected to any voltage in the range 0 to 12V. In the figure, R_{LO} is connected to 0V and R_{HI} is connected to the internal reference, with output V_{OUT} at pin 7, nominally 1.25V. With this wiring, the voltage ranges between 0V and 1.25V and is divided into 10 steps of 0.125V each. When the input is 0V, no LEDs are lit. As input rises above 0.125V the first LED comes on. The

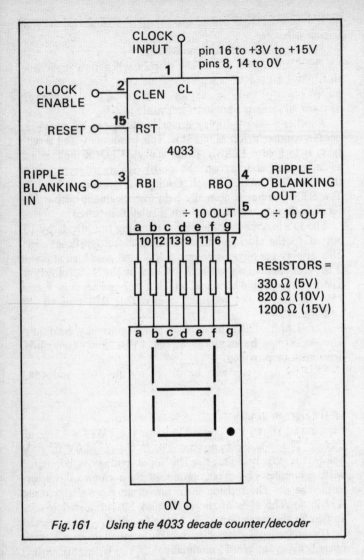

Fig.161   Using the 4033 decade counter/decoder

second LED comes on when the voltage has risen to 0.25V, and so on until all 10 LEDs are lit when input is 1.25V. This happens if the ic is in *bar mode* with the mode select pin 9

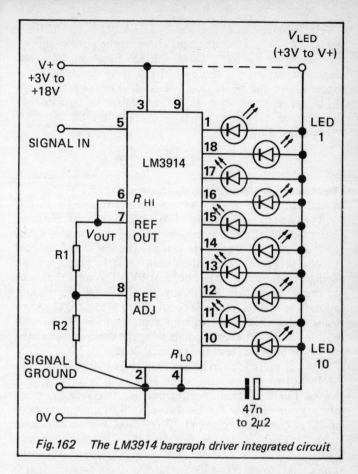

Fig.162   The LM3914 bargraph driver integrated circuit

wired to +V as shown. If pin 9 is left unconnected, the ic is in *dot mode* and only one LED is lit at a time (there is a certain amount of 'overlap' so that the LEDs are not all 'off' at the changeover).

The reference voltage can be adjusted within a limited range by varying the values of R1 and R2. First decide on the value of R1, since this also acts as an LED brightness control. The LED current is approximately:

$$R1 = 12.5/I_{LED}$$

For example, with a current of 15mA, R1 = 12.5/0.015 = 833Ω. V_{LED} can be connected either to the positive supply, as shown, or to some *lower* voltage, minimum 3V. The capacitor in series with the LEDs is there to stabilise the operation of the circuit, and is needed when the leads to the LEDs are relatively long. If leads are short, this capacitor can be omitted. Next, calculate R2, depending on the value required for V_{OUT}:

$$V_{OUT} = 1.25 (1 + R2/R1)$$

Thus, for V_{OUT} = 1.25V as described above, R2 = 0, i.e. pin 8 and the lower end of R1 are connected directly to 0V.

The same principles apply when using an external reference. For example, if pin 6 is held at 10V and pin 4 is at 0V, the LED scale is 1 LED per volt. It is also possible to add resistors to one or both ends of the chain, so as to obtain a more limited range that does not begin at 0V. The total resistance of the internal chain is typically 10kΩ, though, due to variation in tolerance, it may lie between 6.5kΩ and 15kΩ. When using external resistors, connect a capacitor in parallel with each of them. Voltage at points along the chain are calculated by using the principle of the potential divider (p.77).

Two or more ic's can be cascaded to give displays of 20 or more LEDs. Connect the mode input (pin 9) of the first ic to the LED1 pin (pin 1) of the next ic. Continue this along the cascade until the last ic. Leave pin 9 of this open for dot mode or connect it to pin 11. Wire a 20kΩ resistor in parallel with LED9 for all ic's except the last. Connect the resistor chains of all ic's in series to make one long chain. Apply the input signal to pin 5 of all ic's.

This ic is also available in two other versions. In the 3915 the internal resistor chain is graded so that the ic gives a logarithmic response. The steps are 3dB, i.e. a doubling of input voltage for every two LEDs. If the full-scale voltage is 10V (0dB), with 10 LEDs lit, the voltage required to illuminate n LEDs is given by $V_{FSD} \times 0.7071^{10-n}$. For example, 9 LEDs are lit when the input is $10 \times 0.7071^1 = 7.071$V. Another example: 5 LEDs are lit at $10 \times 0.7071^5 = 1.77$V. If voltage is increased steadily from 0V to 10V, the LEDs light up in rapid succession at first, but more slowly later. The 3916 has a response suited to a VU-meter; the steps indicated by the LEDs are: −10dB, −7dB, −5dB, −3dB, −1dB, 0dB, 1dB, 2dB and 3dB.

The LED outputs are open-collector and can be used to drive TTL or CMOS logic circuits instead. In this case, a pull-up resistor is required at each output.

22 Liquid crystal displays

Deciding between LEDs and liquid crystal displays

In selecting a display other than a meter (see p.67) the decision rests between the two most commonly used display techniques, light-emitting diodes and liquid crystal displays. The most important criteria for choosing between these are:

Feature	LED display	LCD
Visibility in dark or dim light	Excellent	Needs a backlight
Visibility in bright light	Poor	Excellent
Power requirements	High	Very low
Driving circuit	None	30−200Hz oscillator required
Format	Individual LEDs of many shapes and colours; single 7-segment and dot-matrix displays allow great flexibility of layout	Mainly standardised displays of 4 or more digits or alphanumeric characters; plus standard symbols

The final section of this table implies that LCD displays are suitable for conventional applications, including very complicated ones but, if something a little out of the ordinary is required, LEDs are more likely to provide it. There seems to be no LCD equivalent of the single LED or the LED bar array.

7-segment LCD display driver

An LCD driving circuit must provide for the driven segments of the display alternately to be more positive than and more negative than the back-plane, otherwise the electrodes of the display become plated and eventually the device ceases to function. The 4056 provides such outputs by means of the DISPLAY FREQUENCY IN (DFI) input. The segment outputs, when active, are out of phase with this input. Thus, three possible modes of operation are possible with this ic:

Pin 6 to	Outputs	Drives
0V	Active-high	Common cathode LED
Positive supply	Active-low	Common anode LED
Square-wave 0V-positive	Alternating	LCD

When used for LCD driving, as in Figure 163, the DFI is fed with a square wave signal with frequency between 30Hz and 200Hz. This is provided by an astable which can conveniently be built from two inverter gates (p.217), as precision is unimportant. The outputs driving the *active* segments are 180° *out of phase* with the signal at pin 6. Consequently there is an alternating voltage across the active segments, which appear black. The outputs driving the *inactive* segments are *in phase* with the signal at pin 6 and the result is that no potential difference appears between the backplane and the segments. The display remains clear. This ic produces tails on 6 and 9, as in Figure 159(b).

The STROBE input controls the latching action of the ic. When STROBE is high, the output follows the data inputs. When it is low, the data is latched and the most recent set of data is held on the LCD.

A similar ic, the 4543, does not require the negative −5V supply. The pinout is the same as that of the 4056, except that pin 7 is used as a display-blanking input.

The 7448 (or a 7447 with pull-up resistors on its outputs) can be used to drive an LCD, but the necessary alternating field must be provided externally, as it has no DFI. The

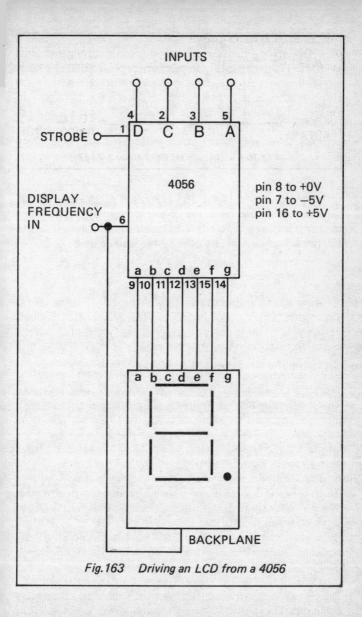

Fig. 163   Driving an LCD from a 4056

283

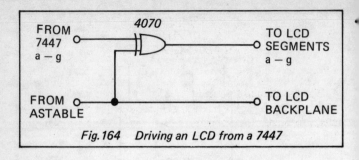

Fig. 164   Driving an LCD from a 7447

technique shown in Figure 164 makes use of an exclusive-OR
gate on every line from the ic to the display.   The extra
circuitry involved makes this an uneconomic solution unless
the ripple blanking facility of the 7448 is to be used.

Chapter 5

RADIO CIRCUITS

1 Wavelength and frequency

The velocity of radio waves is the same as for other forms of electromagnetic radiation, 3×10^8 ms^{-1}. The wavelength λ for any given frequency f is given by:

$$\lambda = \frac{3 \times 10^8}{f}$$

where λ is in metres and f is in hertz. Radio wavelengths are conventionally divided into a number of bands, dependent on frequency or wavelength, as shown in Table 22. Also shown are the allocated broadcasting bands in the United Kingdom.

2 Aerials and antennae

(i) Longwire aerial: This consists of a length of multi-stranded insulated wire, supported by insulators at both ends. It should preferably be 10–40m long and held at least 3m above ground level. An earth connection on the receiver improves the performance with this type of aerial. It is more-or-less omni-directional. A down-lead to the receiver is connected at one end; this may be the same wire as is used for the aerial.

(ii) Half-wave dipole: Consists of two wires supported by insulators at each end, and leading to a 75Ω coaxial cable (Fig.165(a)). An earth connection is not needed. For selective reception on a given wavelength, the overall length of the aerial is approximately 0.475λ. If mounted horizontally, reception is best from either side of the dipole, least from the direction in line with the wires. Except on the shortest wavebands, the length of this and the other dipoles described below becomes prohibitively long (see Section 3 below).

Table 22 — WAVELENGTH AND FREQUENCY

Frequency		Wavelength		Name	Abbreviation
10	30kHz	30km	10km	Very-low frequency	VLF
30	300kHz	10km	1km	Low frequency	LF
300	3000kHz	1000m	100m	Medium frequency	MF
3	30MHz	100m	10m	High frequency	HF
30	300MHz	10m	1m	Very-high frequency	VHF
300	3000MHz	1000mm	100mm	Ultra-high frequency	UHF
3	30GHz	100mm	10mm	Super-high frequency	SHF
30	300GHz	10mm	1mm	Extremely-high frequency	EHF

BROADCASTING BANDS

Frequency		Wavelength		Frequency description	Band name	Uses
148.5	283.5kHz	2020	1058m	LF	Long wave	a.m. radio
526.5	1606.5kHz	570	187m	MF	Medium wave	a.m. radio
87.5	108MHz	3.4	2.8m	VHF	Band II	f.m. radio
470	582MHz	630	520mm	UHF	Band IV	TV (21–34)
614	854MHz	490	350mm	UHF	Band V	TV (39–68)
11.7	12.5GHz	26	24mm	SHF	Band VI	Satellite TV

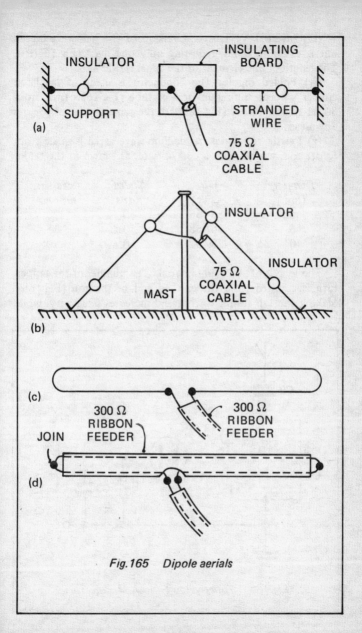

Fig. 165   Dipole aerials

287

(iii) Inverted V: This is a version of the half-wave dipole but is easier to build, requiring only one mast (Fig.165(b)). The length of one element of the aerial is 0.25λ.

(iv) Folded dipole: The conductor is made of insulated copper wire or aluminium rod or tube (Fig.165(c)) or from 300Ω ribbon feeder (Fig.165(d)), the same as is used for the downlead.

(v) Ferrite rod aerial: A medium-wave aerial is made from ferrite rod, wound with a coil of wire, as shown in the table:

Diameter (mm)	Wire (swg)	No. of turns	Tap at turn no.
6.5	36–38	80	20
8	36–38	70	15
10	28–32	60	10

The length of rod is immaterial. The number of the tapped turn is counted from the earthed end of the coil (Fig.166). Making the tap nearer to that end increases selectivity, while

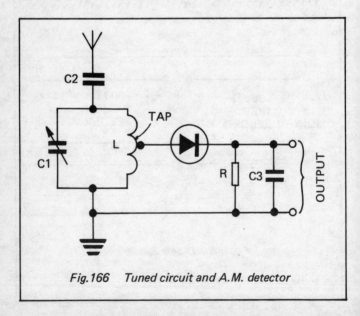

Fig.166   Tuned circuit and A.M. detector

making it nearer the other end increases the sensitivity. The capacitor C2 and aerial shown in Figure 166 are not required. Mount the rod horizontally; strongest signals are received from directions perpendicular to the axis of the rod.

3 Aerial amplifiers

Reception is improved if the signal from the aerial is passed to a wide-band amplifier. The simple amplifier in Figure 167(a) is suitable for amplifying the signal from small aerials such as a metal rod, a telescopic aerial or a short wire.

A similar amplifier appears three times in Figure 167(b), amplifying the signal from the two halves of a dipole aerial. Use of such an amplifier means that it is unnecessary for the aerial to be as long as indicated in sections 2(ii) to (iv) above. The short dipole elements, which can be supported wires or metal tubes or rods, are orientated in line, with the amplifier between them. The variable resistor is for balancing the two halves of the amplifier so that any common signal received by the two halves of the dipole can be cancelled out, thus improving directivity. The transformer T1 consists of two coils of 9 turns (primary) and 22 turns (secondary) 24 swg enamelled copper wire wound on an iron dust toroid 12.7mm external diameter. The turns are held in place with epoxy resin adhesive which is also used to glue the toroid to the pcb. Alternatively, use a ready-made RF transformer wound on a ferrite core, with a similar turns ratio.

To adjust the amplifier, first short the dipole elements together at the point where they connect with the amplifier. Tune the receiver to a strong local station, then adjust VR1 until the minimum volume is obtained. Disconnect the shorting wire. If the dipole is mounted with its elements vertical it receives signals more or less equally from all directions. If they are horizontal, reception is directional.

4 Tuned circuit

A simple AM tuned circuit is shown to the left of Figure 166. This consists of a variable capacitor C1 and an inductor, L. As already mentioned, the coil may be wound on a ferrite rod,

289

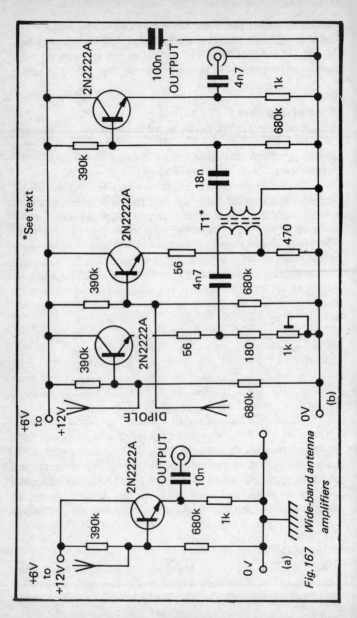

Fig. 167 Wide-band antenna amplifiers

which then acts as an aerial. It may instead be a coil with a core of air, ferrite or iron dust. In this case an external aerial is needed, coupled to the tuning circuit by capacitor C2, which should be no more than 100pF. The tuned frequency is given by:

$$f = \frac{1}{2\pi \sqrt{LC}}$$

where C is the capacitance of C1, and L is the self-inductance of the coil. A suitable coil may be bought ready-made, or wound by hand on a former (see p.29). A core of ferrite or an iron dust core increases the self-inductance. The resistance of the wire of the coil tends to reduce the Q of the coil, making it less selective. For this reason wind the coil from the thickest possible wire that the former will accommodate, e.g. 16 or 18 swg.

5 Detector circuit

A simple AM detector appears on the right of Figure 166. The detecting element is the diode, preferably a germanium point-contact diode such as an AA119, OA90 or OA95. This circuit also includes a resistor and capacitor to demodulate the radio frequency signal. R is about 2.2kΩ and C3 is between 220nF and 4.7μF. Crystal earphones may be connected directly to the output terminals, or the signal may be amplified by an audio amplifier.

6 Radio-frequency amplifiers

An amplifier which can be used as an aerial amplifier or at a later stage is illustrated in Figure 168. This is a common-emitter amplifier with an inductor in the collector circuit to improve its response at high frequencies. The value of the inductor is best found by trial, but is usually between 10μH and 470μH.

A similar circuit (Fig.169) has a tuned circuit in series with the collector. The circuit preferentially amplifies frequencies centred on the frequency of the tuned circuit, calculated as described above.

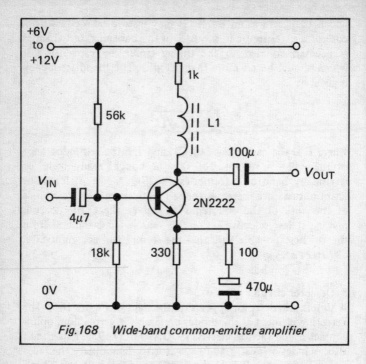

Fig. 168   Wide-band common-emitter amplifier

7 Radio-frequency filters

In contrast to audio-frequency filter (p.120) radio-frequency
filters are usually built from capacitors and inductors. The
high frequencies mean that inductors can be small so that the
objection to them on grounds of size does not apply. The
main problem is the possibility of electromagnetic interference, either between inductors or between an inductor and
other parts of the circuit. This must be attended to when
laying out the circuit. Space inductors well apart and, if
necessary, enclose them in screening cans.

Figure 170 illustrates the commonly-used T-section and
π-section low-pass and high-pass filters. The π-section filter
is often preferred but, if the load (output) impedance is
greater than the source (input) impedance, the T-section
should be used. For the 3-pole filters shown in Figure 170
the −3dB cut-off frequency is given by:

292

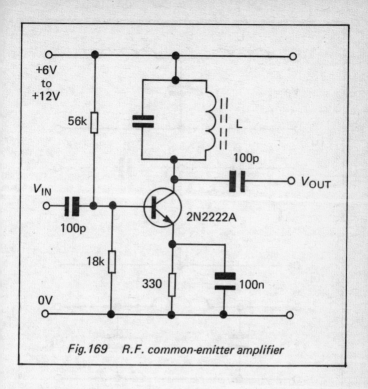

Fig.169   R.F. common-emitter amplifier

$$f_c = \frac{1}{2\pi \sqrt{LC}}$$

Given a value of f_c, calculate suitable values for L and C, then use components of values L/2, L or 2L, and C/2, C or 2C, as indicated in the figure.

Butterworth low-pass LC filters
The T-section or π-section filters may be cascaded to build filters with an increased roll-off in the transition region. Figure 171 shows a 7-pole low-pass filter built in this way ($n = 7$). Under this scheme, the filters of Figure 170 have 3 poles ($n = 3$). The table below gives the factors required for designing π-section low-pass filters of any number of

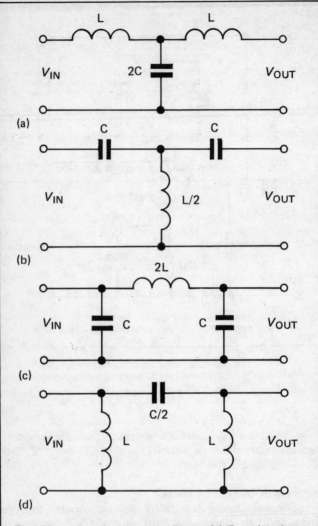

Fig. 170   LC radio-frequency filters: (a) T-section, low-
            pass; (b) T-section, high-pass; (c) π-section, low-
            pass; (d) π-section, high pass

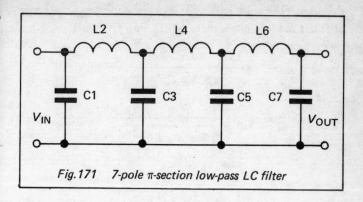

Fig. 171   7-pole π-section low-pass LC filter

poles from $n = 2$ to $n = 7$. These filters have a Butterworth response, i.e. a very flat passband. As mentioned earlier, these filters are suitable when the source and load impedances are equal or when the source impedance is greater than the load impedance.

n	C1	L2	C3	L4	C5	L6	C7
2	1.4142	1.4142					
3	1.0000	2.0000	1.0000				
4	0.7654	1.8478	1.8478	0.7654			
5	0.6180	1.6180	2.0000	1.6180	0.6180		
6	0.5176	1.4142	1.9319	1.9319	1.4142	0.5176	
7	0.4450	1.2470	1.8019	2.0000	1.8019	1.2470	0.4450

The value of each capacitor is calculated from:

$$C = \frac{\text{factor}}{2\pi f_c R}$$

where R is the load resistance and f_c is the cut-off frequency. The value of each inductor is calculated from:

$$L = \frac{R \times \text{factor}}{2\pi f_c}$$

295

Example: Design a 5-pole low-pass filter for source impedance of 50kΩ and load impedance of 1kΩ, with f_c = 1MHz.

$$C1 = C5 = \frac{0.6180}{2 \times \pi \times 1 \times 10^6 \times 1 \times 10^3} = 98\text{pF}$$

$$L2 = L4 = \frac{1 \times 10^3 \times 1.6180}{2 \times \pi \times 1 \times 10^6} = 257\mu\text{H}$$

$$C3 = \frac{2}{2 \times \pi \times 1 \times 10^6 \times 1 \times 10^3} = 318\text{pF}$$

For non-critical applications, C1 = C5 = 100pF, L2 = L4 = 250μH and C3 = 330pF.

The table below gives the factors for designing T-section low-pass filters. These are for use when source and load impedances are equal or when the load impedance is greater than that of the source.

n	L1	C2	L3	C4	L5	C6	L7
2	1.4142	1.4142					
3	1.0000	2.0000	1.0000				
4	0.7654	1.8478	1.8478	0.7654			
5	0.6180	1.6180	2.0000	1.6180	0.6180		
6	0.5176	1.4142	1.9319	1.9319	1.4142	0.5176	
7	0.4450	1.2470	1.8019	2.0000	1.8019	1.2470	0.4450

The procedure for using this table for designing low-pass filters is as above.

Butterworth high-pass LC filters

The filters have the same configuration as in Figure 171 but with capacitors and inductors exchanged. In this case the T-section is usually preferred when source and load impedances are equal. The formulae for calculating capacitor and inductor values are:

$$C = \frac{1}{2\pi f_c R \times \text{factor}}$$

$$L = \frac{R}{2\pi f_c \times \text{factor}}$$

The factors are taken from the tables, as before, except that 'L' and 'C' are swapped in the headings. For example, 'L1' now reads as 'C1' and 'C2' now reads as 'L2'.

Example: Design a 5-pole high-pass filter for source impedance of 50kΩ and load impedance of 1kΩ, with f_c = 1MHz. This is π-section filter, so we use the first table above.

$$L1 = L5 = \frac{1 \times 10^3}{2 \times \pi \times 1 \times 10^6 \times 0.6180} = 257\mu H$$

$$C2 = C4 = \frac{1}{2 \times \pi \times 1 \times 10^6 \times 1 \times 10^3 \times 1.6180} = 98pF$$

$$L3 = \frac{1 \times 10^3}{2 \times \pi \times 1 \times 10^6 \times 2} = 79\mu H$$

Band-pass and notch filters

The centre frequencies of the simple filters shown in Figure 172 are calculated by using the formula:

$$f_c = \frac{1}{2\pi \sqrt{LC}}$$

The response of such filters peaks or dips sharply at f_c. To design a Butterworth bandpass filter with flat pass-band and steeper cut-off (Fig.173), first decide on the cut-off points, f_{CL} and f_{CH}, then calculate the centre frequency:

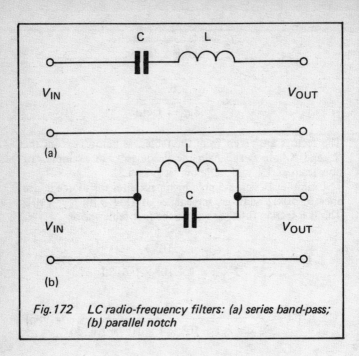

Fig.172   LC radio-frequency filters: (a) series band-pass;
(b) parallel notch

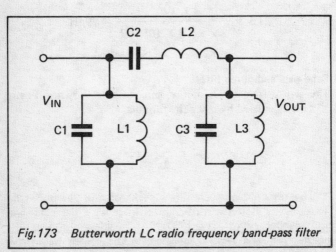

Fig.173   Butterworth LC radio frequency band-pass filter

$$f_{0'} = \sqrt{f_{CL} \times f_{CH}}$$

Next calculate the values of C1, C3 and L2 as if this was to be a 3-pole low-pass π-section filter (p.295), with frequency equal to the *bandwidth* of the band-pass filter. For each of these values calculate the value of the corresponding inductors (L1, L3) and capacitor (C2) so that each of the inductor/capacitor pairs resonates at f_0. The formula for resonance is the same as that given above for f_c.

Example: Design a 3-pole bandpass filter, f_{CL} = 16MHz, f_{CH} = 20MHz, for source and load impedances of 50Ω.

$$f_0 = \sqrt{16 \times 20} = 17.9\text{MHz} \qquad \text{(all in MHz)}$$

$$\text{bandwidth} = 4\text{MHz}$$

$$C1 = C3 = \frac{1}{2\pi \times 4 \times 10^6 \times 50} = 796\text{pF}$$

$$L2 = \frac{50}{2\pi \times 4 \times 10^6} = 1.98\mu\text{H}$$

Now calculate the values required for resonance:

$$L1 = L3 = \frac{1}{4\pi^2 f_0^2 C1} = 99\text{nH}$$

$$C2 = \frac{1}{4\pi^2 f_0^2 L2} = 40\text{pF}$$

Chapter 6

POWER SUPPLIES

1 Cells and Batteries
In the comparisons below the term 'capacity' refers to the power storage capacity of a cell in ampere-hours. The voltage given is the nominal fully-charged e.m.f. of a single cell.

Types of cell
(i) Zinc carbon: Have the cheapest cost *per cell* though approximately equal in price to other primary cells in terms of cost *per ampere hour*; high internal resistance (low current); poor shelf life; prone to leakage.

Voltage: 1.5V.

Applications: low power *intermittent* use (a few hours per day), e.g. radio receivers, torches; partly recover if rested.

(ii) Zinc chloride: About 40% more power per cell than zinc carbon cells, but unit price per cell is higher; lower internal resistance (higher current), often sold as heavy duty cells; longer shelf life so may last twice as long as zinc carbon in intermittent use; little risk of leakage.

Voltage: 1.5V.

Applications: medium power intermittent use, for example doorbells, tape players, hand lamps; also good for lower power *continuous drain* uses such as clocks.

(iii) Alkaline: 2.5 to 3 times as much power per cell as zinc carbon cells; low internal resistance (high current); long shelf life; virtually leak-free.

Voltage: 1.5V.

Applications: medium to high power intermittent or continuous use, such as flashguns, toys, radios which are switched on for many hours at a time.

(iv) Silver oxide: Low power, long-lasting, stable output.

Voltage: 1.5V.

Applications: mainly in the form of button cells for use in small items of equipment such as watches and calculators.

(v) Mercury oxide: Similar to silver oxide cells in characteristics and applications. All are button cells.

Voltage: 1.35V.

(vi) Lithium: Provide very low currents or high-power bursts (up to 30A); lifetime of several years. High energy density (i.e. large capacity in small volume).

Voltage: 3V.

Applications: motorised cameras, computer memory back-up.

(vii) Lead acid: Very low internal resistance (very high current, tens of amps); may be kept fully charged by trickle charging; they can be left unused for long periods without deterioration; but must not be left in the fully discharged condition. Sealed types are preferred for safety and convenience.

Voltage: 2V, usually available as 6V or 12V batteries.

Applications: high-current uses such as starter motors, automobile headlamps, infrequent uses such as doorbells, standby batteries for security systems.

(viii) Nickel cadmium: Low capacity, about 20% of a zinc carbon cell; rechargeable, can be trickle-charged; low internal resistance (high-current); discharge when left standing; can be left in discharged state.

Voltage: 1.2V.

Applications: high-current frequent use, such as electric razors, personal stereos.

Lead acid and nickel cadmium cells are marketed as rechargeable cells. They can be recharged several hundred times. Zinc carbon, zinc chloride and alkaline cells are usually described by manufacturers as being non-rechargeable. However, given a suitable charging circuit which periodically reverses the polarity of the charging current (unlike the chargers used for lead acid and nickel cadmium cells), they can be recharged 20 or more times.

2 Mains-powered supplies

Use of mains power inevitably presents safety problems, both to the constructor and also to persons using equipment that is powered from the mains. The novice constructor should not

attempt to build mains-powered circuits without taking advice
from an experienced person. A wide range of ready-built
power units is available, often at a cost which is less than that
which the constructor would pay for the individual components. For this reason and for the greater safety arising from
using a factory-made unit, such a unit is to be preferred to
one assembled by the constructor. PSUs commonly available
fall under one of these headings:

Bench supplies

A wide range of units is available, capable of supplying current
of several amperes and featuring one or more selected voltages
or a variable voltage output. They may provide for a switchable or variable dual supply, suitable for op amps. Some have
a regulated output, some have current-limiting, some have
meters to display the voltage and current.

Mains adaptors

Often known as battery eliminators; they are cheaply mass-
produced. They are often contained in a large 13-amp plug,
so that the unit plugs directly into a mains socket. Their
output voltage is often switchable to values in multiples of
1.5V, the usual voltages being 3V, 4.5V, 6V, 7.5V, 9V and
12V. Maximum current of the cheaper units is only 300mA,
though this is sufficient for very many home-built circuits.
Units are available with higher current ratings, such as
500mA and 1A.

The majority of such units are unregulated; this may cause
problems if the current drawn is small, since the output may
then be as much as 30% more than the nominal voltage. At
the full rated output current, the voltage may fall slightly
below the nominal level. Another problem with such units is
that they are not protected against excessive current drain.
Connecting them to a circuit which requires current higher
than the maximum rating of the PSU is likely to burn out
the unit. The same may occur if the output is accidentally
short-circuited. These problems are avoided in the more
expensive units which have a regulated output. Unregulated
units are usable in many uncritical applications and it is easy
to protect the unit and stabilise its output by using a voltage

regulator, as explained in the next section. Also available are adaptors with a.c. output; unless the power circuit is able to operate on a.c., the output of such adaptors will need to be rectified.

Open or encapsulated units
These are ready-built units intended for building into projects. They are often intended for soldering directly to the main pcb of the project. Open units are the equivalent of the power unit a constructor would build and may have exposed parts at mains voltage. The encapsulated units afford greater safety, it being necessary only to guard against mains voltages where the mains leads run to the terminals of the unit, and around power switches. The remarks on mains power and safety at the beginning of this section apply to all units of this type.

DC-DC units
These convert a d.c. supply at one voltage into a d.c. supply at another voltage. An example of this is the simple circuit for converting a positive voltage into an equal negative voltage, given on page 88. Ready-made DC-DC converters have a greater current output than the simple circuit and better stability. The most commonly available units require an input of +5V or +12V and produce one or more regulated outputs such as ±5V, +12V, and ±12V, and ±15V.

3 Improving the performance of mains adators

Transient suppressors
These absorb transient voltage peaks on the mains supply, preventing them from passing to the PSU and through to the circuit. They are wired across the mains supply (Fig.174). A suppressor can be enclosed in a mains plug, with its terminal wires secured in the live and neutral screw terminals of the plug. The plug is inserted in a socket adjacent to that used by the mains PSU. Mains transient suppressors are rated to withstand 240V and must not be confused with suppressor capacitors, contact suppressors, r.f. suppressors and motor suppressors, all of which are unsuited for this application.

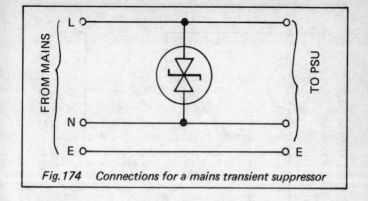

Fig.174   Connections for a mains transient suppressor

L ○ — — — — — — — ○
FROM MAINS
N ○ — — — — — — — ○
E ○ — — — — — — — ○ E
TO PSU

Rectification

This is possible only for PSUs with a.c. output. For most purposes a 4-diode bridge is preferred (Fig.175), either using four separate rectifier diodes (p.32) or a ready-made bridge. Diodes or bridges are selected to pass the required maximum current. For reliability, it is better to use components rated to pass double the expected maximum. The diodes produce a voltage drop of twice their forward voltage drop, i.e. a total of 1.2V. This point needs taking into account when rectifying current from a low-voltage PSU, particularly if a voltage regulator is to be used, as there may not be sufficient 'headroom' to power the regulator.

The figure shows where a transient suppressor may be inserted as an alternative to connecting it across the mains supply. This is a better position, as the suppressor is itself protected by being on the secondary side of the transformer where currents are lower. It needs to be rated only to withstand the lower (transformed) voltage.

Smoothing

To reduce manufacturing costs and also to make it possible to house the circuit in a case of modest size, certain plug-in adaptors have insufficient smoothing. This shows up as increased ripple voltage as current consumption increases. It may be remedied by connecting a large-value capacitor across the supply (Fig.176). The formula for calculating the

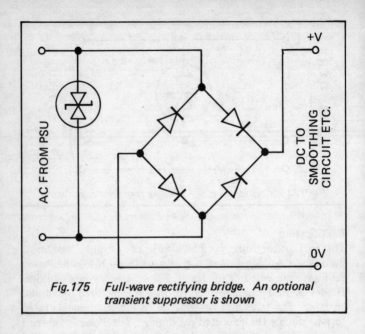

Fig. 175   Full-wave rectifying bridge.   An optional
transient suppressor is shown

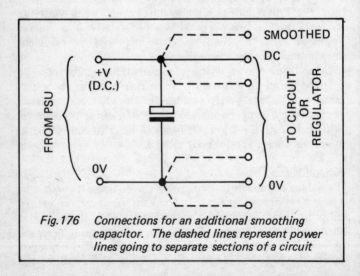

Fig. 176   Connections for an additional smoothing
capacitor.   The dashed lines represent power
lines going to separate sections of a circuit

value is:

$$C = I_{LOAD}/V_{RIPPLE} \times t$$

t is 8ms for 50Hz supplies and 6ms for 60Hz. Smoothing is applicable only to d.c. PSUs.

Example: I_{LOAD} = 500mA, the supply is 50Hz, and the permitted ripple voltage is 0.2V. Thus C = 20000μF. Use a 22000μF electrolytic capacitor with working voltage at least twice that of the PSU output voltage. Since mains adaptors run at 1A or less, ripple current is not usually a problem with capacitors as large as those required for smoothing.

When several sections of a circuit are to be connected to the smoothing capacitor, the power and ground lines should all be taken to common points close to the terminals of the capacitor (Fig.176). If this is not done, ripple current introduces hum into the circuit. This raises a general point that applies not only to power supply lines but to other circuit connections as well. When laying out pcb's, or planning wiring between a power supply and a pcb, or between two pcb's, it is important to avoid *loops*. These occur where there are *two* (or more) conductive pathways from one point in the circuit to another. The loop acts as an inductor 'coil' and currents are induced in it by stray electromagnetic radiation. This can result in unwanted hum, or the production of voltage spikes which may upset the operation of the circuit.

Voltage regulation

For low-current non-critical regulation use a Zener diode circuit, as described on page 80. For other applications a 3-terminal series regular ic is the usual choice. Figure 177 shows the circuit for fixed-voltage regulation, using one of the popular 78/79 series regulators. The first two digits of the type number specify polarity: 78 for positive regulators, 79 for negative regulators. The final two digits specify the regulated voltage: 05, 06, 08, 09, 12, 15, 18, or 24. The type number may also include a code letter such as 'L', for low power (100mA, e.g. 78L05), 'M' for medium power (500mA), 'S' for super power (2A) and 'H' for the hybrid regulators which provide up to 5A of power. The standard

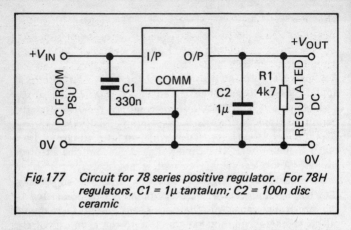

Fig.177 *Circuit for 78 series positive regulator. For 78H regulators, C1 = 1µ tantalum; C2 = 100n disc ceramic*

regulators operate at up to 1A and usually have no code letter (e.g. 7805 for a 5V, 1A positive regulator). Although details vary from manufacturer to manufacturer, the specifications of most types is as follows:

Precision: ±4%
Maximum supply voltage: 30V–40V
Minimum supply voltage: about 2.5V above the regulated voltage.
Line regulation: Maximum 1% but less than 0.5% for many types.
Load regulation: Maximum 2% but less than 0.5% for many types and considerably less (0.2%) for some.
Ripple rejection: 50dB–80dB.
Quiescent current: 1mA–5mA.
Output resistance: 0.2Ω or less.

All regulators incorporate current limiting with fold-back (if excessive current is drawn the output voltage falls to restrict current to appreciably less than the rated maximum), and thermal shut-down (cuts out if over-heated).

Figure 177 shows the circuit for the 78 regulators: that for the 79 regulators is identical except that $+V_{IN}$ and $+V_{OUT}$ are replaced by the negative voltages. The 330n capacitor must be soldered to the circuit board as close as possible to the terminal pins of the regulator. The resistor provides a minimum load for times when the regulator is not supplying current to a circuit but this may be dispensed with if the circuit continuously draws current. In addition, a transient suppressor may be wired on the input side of this circuit, if not already included on the mains or transformed supply (see above). The 100mA regulators do not require heat sinks but a higher-rated regulator will nearly always need one. The power dissipation is approximately calculated from:

$$P = (V_{\text{SUPPLY}} - V_{\text{REG}}) \times I_{\text{LOAD}}$$

For this reason the supply voltage should not be more than 5V or 6V above the regulator output voltage. Given the power dissipation and that the intrinsic (junction-to-case) thermal resistance θ_1 is $3°C/W$ for 78/79 regulators, the size of heat sink required can be calculated as on page 72.

Fixed voltages other than those for which a regulator is available may be obtained by wiring the regulator as in Figure 178. There is some reduction in regulation but this arrangement is adequate for most purposes. The required resistors are calculated from the formula:

$$\frac{R1}{R2} = \frac{V_{\text{REG}} + 0.6}{V_{\text{OUT}} - V_{\text{REG}} - 0.6}$$

Example: to produce a 7.5V supply, use a 7805: R1/R2 = 5.6/1.9 = 2.95. Let R1 = 2.2kΩ, then R2 = R1/2.95 = 750Ω.

If R1 and R2 are replaced by a variable resistor, a variable output voltage is obtained. For easier adjusting, the variable resistor may have a fixed resistor in series with it at either or both ends. The essence of the circuit is to have a potential divider (p.77) between the output of the regulator and the 0V rail. If V_P is the voltage at the wiper of the variable resistor, then:

$$V_{\text{OUT}} = V_{\text{REG}} + V_P + 0.6$$

Figure 179 shows the terminal designations of the 78/79 series.

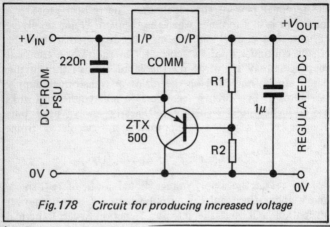

Fig.178   Circuit for producing increased voltage

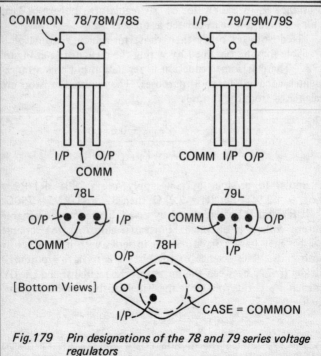

Fig.179   Pin designations of the 78 and 79 series voltage regulators

723 variable voltage regulator

This 14-pin ic operates on a d.c. supply up to +40V and produces an output voltage in the range 2V to 37V, with a maximum output current of 150mA. Line regulation is 0.1%, load regulation is 0.6%, ripple rejection is 74dB, and it has current limiting. Figure 180 shows the ic connected for outputs in the range 2V to 7V. It has its own voltage reference at pin 6. The resistor values are calculated from:

$$V_{OUT} = V_{REF} \times \frac{R2}{R1 + R2}$$

$$R3 = \frac{R1 \times R2}{R1 + R2}$$

If R1 and R2 are replaced by a variable resistor, V_{OUT} can be varied over the lower range 2V to 7V. As usual, the supply voltage must exceed the required output by at least 3V. Output current may be limited to any value less than 150mA by selection of the value of R_{CS}:

$$R_{CS} = 0.7/I_{LIM}$$

In Figure 181 the ic is connected for output voltages between 7V and 37V. Resistor values are calculated from:

$$V_{OUT} = V_{REF} \times \frac{R1 + R2}{R2}$$

R3 is calculated as above, though it can be replaced by a plain wire link between pins 5 and 6. R_{CS} is calculated as before. Figure 182 shows how to modify either of the above circuits to obtain a larger current. The maximum current then depends upon the rating of the transistor, which is likely to need a heat sink. The current is limited to any required value by selecting a suitable value for R_{CS}, according to the formula previously given.

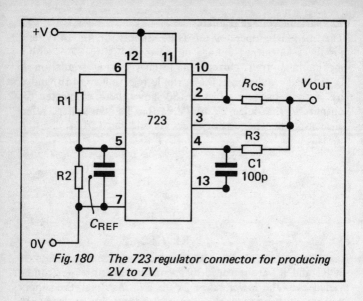

Fig. 180   The 723 regulator connector for producing 2V to 7V

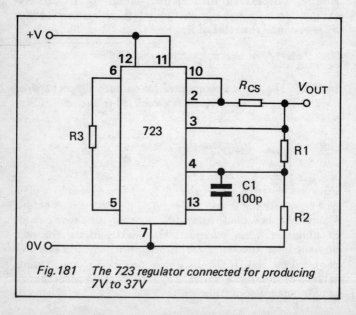

Fig. 181   The 723 regulator connected for producing 7V to 37V

312

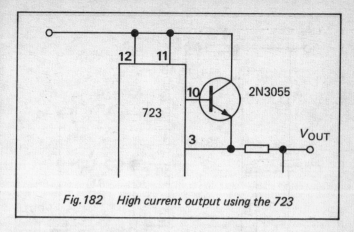

Fig.182   High current output using the 723

Low drop-out regulators

Normally the supply voltage must be 2.5V or more above the regulator output voltage. This can be a serious disadvantage under certain circumstances, for example when trying to run a 5V logic circuit from a 6V battery. For this purpose it is best to employ a regulator specially designed to run with very little drop-out, or 'headroom'. The drop-out voltage increases to a maximum at maximum output current. Examples are:

Type No.	Max. output current (A)	Output voltage	Drop-out (V) average	maximum
LM2940	1	5	0.5	1.0
LT1085CT-5	3	5	1.0	1.5
LT1085CT-12	3	12	1.0	1.5
LT1086CT-5	1.5	5	1.0	1.5
LT1086CT-12	1.5	12	1.0	1.5

Switching regulators

Switching regulators are used to produce a regulated lower voltage, higher voltage, or even a negative voltage, from a low voltage unregulated supply. The supply may come from a battery, or from the mains via a rectifier and smoothing circuit. Several regulators are available, from which we have

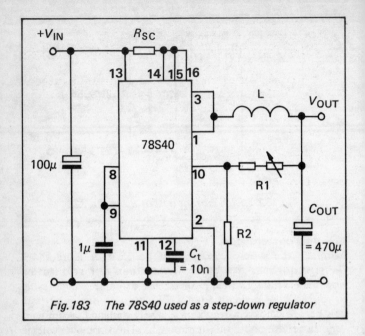

Fig. 183   The 78S40 used as a step-down regulator

selected the 78S40 as being one of the most useful.

The 78S40 operates on a supply voltage between 2.5V and 40V. Its output can be set to any voltage in the range 1.3V to 40V. Its line regulation is 0.04mV/V and its load regulation is 0.2mV/mA. It can supply a current of up to 1.5A, though this can be increased by using an output transistor, as with several other regulators described above. It has output current limiting. The maximum frequency of the oscillator is 75kHz.

The circuit for stepping down a voltage is shown in Figure 183. The procedure for calculating component values is as follows:

Given the input voltage V_{IN}, decide on the output voltage V_{OUT} and the *maximum* output current I_{OUT}.

The figure shows suitable values for the timing capacitor C_T and the output capacitor C_{OUT}.

The stages of calculating component values are:

314

(a) The peak current $I_{PK} = 2 \times I_{OUT}$.

(b) The value of the current-sensing resistor R_{SC} is $0.33/I_{PK}$.

(c) The time for which the current is off, t_{OFF}, depends on the timing capacitor C_T. The equation is:

$$C_T = 45 \times 10^{-5} \times t_{OFF}$$

If $C_T = 10nF$, then $t_{OFF} = 22\mu s$.

(d) The value of the inductor is given by:

$$L = \frac{V_{OUT} + V_D}{I_{PK}} \times t_{OFF}$$

where V_D is the forward voltage drop across the internal diode (pins 1 to 2); $V_D = 1.25V$.

(e) R1 and R2 form a potential divider, which must provide a voltage of 1.245V at pin 10, to match the voltage from the internal voltage reference. Working in kilohms: R1 = R2($V_{OUT}/1.245 - 1$). Since the reference voltage may vary between 1.18V and 1.31V, it is necessary to wire R1 as a fixed resistor and variable resistor in series to allow adjustment of the voltage at pin 10.

Example: Given $V_{IN} = 20V$, $V_{OUT} = 15V$, $I_{OUT} = 0.5A$, $C_T = 10nF$, $C_{OUT} = 470\mu F$. Calculations:

$$I_{PK} = 2 \times 0.5 = 1A$$

$$R_{SC} = 0.33/1 = 0.33\Omega$$

$$L = (15 + 1.25)/1 \times t_{OFF} = 16.25 \times 22 \times 10^{-6} = 358\mu H$$

A 330μH inductor would probably suffice, though it is preferable to use the next largest standard value, 470μH. Take R2 as a convenient value, say 10kΩ.

Then $R1 = 10(15/1.245 - 1) = 110\text{k}\Omega$. Use a $100\text{k}\Omega$ fixed resistor in series with a $22\text{k}\Omega$ preset.

The circuit for stepping up a voltage is shown in Figure 184. The procedure for calculating component values is as follows:

Given the input voltage V_{IN}, decide on the output voltage V_{OUT} and the *maximum* output current I_{OUT}.

The figure shows suitable values for the timing capacitor C_T and the output capacitor C_{OUT}.

The stages of calculating component values are:

(a) The peak current

$$I_{PK} = 2 \times I_{OUT} \times \frac{V_{OUT} + V_D - V_{SAT}}{V_{IN} - V_{SAT}}$$

where $V_D = 1.25\text{V}$, as explained above, and V_{SAT} is the saturated voltage drop across the internal Darlington pair of transistors, typically 1.55V.

(b) The value of the current-sensing resistor R_{SC} is $0.33/I_{PK}$.

(c) The time for which the current is off, t_{OFF}, depends on the timing capacitor C_T. The equation is:

$$C_T = 45 \times 10^{-5} \times t_{OFF}$$

If $C_T = 10\text{nF}$, then $t_{OFF} = 22\mu\text{s}$.

(d) The value of the inductor is given by:

$$L = \frac{V_{OUT} + V_D - V_{IN}}{I_{PK}} \times t_{OFF}$$

(e) R1 and R2 are calculated as above.

Example: Given $V_{IN} = 6\text{V}$, $V_{OUT} = 12\text{V}$, $I_{OUT} = 0.25\text{A}$, $C_T = 10\text{nF}$, $C_{OUT} = 470\mu\text{F}$. Calculations:

316

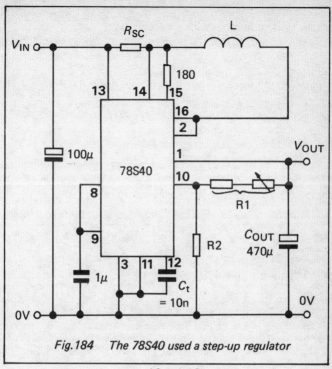

Fig.184   The 78S40 used a step-up regulator

$$I_{PK} = 2 \times 0.25 \times \frac{12 + 1.25 - 1.55}{6 - 1.55} = 1.3A$$

$$R_{SC} = 0.33/1.3 = 0.25\Omega \qquad \text{(use } 0.22\Omega)$$

$$L = (12 + 1.25 - 6)/1.3 \times t_{OFF} = 5.58 \times 22 \times 10^{-6}$$

$$= 123\mu H$$

Use the next largest standard value, $150\mu H$. Take R2 as a convenient value, say $10k\Omega$. Then R1 = $10(12/1.245 - 1)$ = $86k\Omega$. Use a $82k\Omega$ fixed resistor in series with a $10k\Omega$ preset.

For details of further calculations, such as ripple voltage, and for instructions on how to use this ic as a voltage inverter, see the manufacturer's data sheets.

317

Index

Including symbols for physical quantities

T

U